ACT NORMAL

AND DON'T TELL ANYONE ABOUT THE
PRESENT MACHINE

Christian Darkin

Printed in the United Kingdom
First Printing, 2017

The illustrations are by the author, but use some elements for which I'd like to credit and thank: www.obsidiandawn.com, kuschelirmel-stock, and waywardgal

Anachronistic Publishing
www.anachronistic.co.uk/publishing

Part 1:

Act Normal And Don't Tell Anyone
About the Present Machine

Chapter 1

So, we were running. Well, I was running, and Adam was running in front (because he is much faster than me). Granny was not running. Granny was in her wheelchair and it was an electric one, so it was really, really slow.

I knew that this wouldn't do because the doctors were chasing us, and they were very fast because doctors are very busy and used to running around, and emergencies, and not resting, so their legs are very strong.

The thing about electric wheelchairs is that they actually should be very fast. I know this because I once made a racing car out of the engine from one and it was actually faster than a cheetah (there was an escaped cheetah, because of something Adam had done, but that was in a different story, and anyway, I caught it, and it hardly attacked anyone).

The thing is, electric wheelchairs have very strong motors, but they're deliberately slowed down because the people that make wheelchairs imagine that the people that use wheelchairs want to do everything slowly. They should ask them, because, really, people in wheelchairs are often in a big rush. That's probably what this story is about - people thinking they know what other people want - but I'm getting ahead of myself.

All you have to do to get a wheelchair to go fast is to flip open the box with the motor in it, and take out the "slowing down" gears. This is really difficult to do while you're running away from about twenty doctors, and you have to make sure your fingers don't get caught in the gears, or they will get squashed, and then torn off, and then you will need the doctors.

I managed it, just about, and instantly, the wheelchair zoomed. I was just about holding on, but I steered us to follow Adam. Together we smashed through the big double doors at the front of the hospital, with the doctors running out only a couple of seconds behind. Granny was bouncing about in the chair, holding on as tight as she could.

We -

Actually, stop.

I'm telling it wrong. You don't even know why we're running or anything yet, do you? Also, I've not really said anything about Granny. Granny could just be any old lady, and that's not right. You really need to know a lot more about Granny, and who she is, before I can tell you anything about why we're running.

Let's go back a bit. Let's go back to before the fairies became evil, and the books turned against us.

How can I tell you about what kind of a granny Granny is? I know, let's start with her birthday party. Because Granny's birthday party was awful. And it was also the most fun I've had in ages...

Chapter 2

People in this story:

Me: I am Jenny. I'm interested in most things. I usually like birthday parties, but not with rubbish games or real monsters in them. I like experiments, and sometimes my experiments get a bit out of control. That's probably why people say I'm not normal. I do sometimes try to act normal so that they leave me alone to fix the things that have gone out of control. Acting normal is the most difficult thing about being me because I don't really know what normal is supposed to be like. I think that secretly everybody is not normal, and secretly everybody is pretending. I think, sometimes, grown-ups have spent so long acting normal that they forget they're pretending, and I think those people are the weirdest ones.

Adam: Adam is my little brother. Adam's favourite thing is chaos. He is very good at it, and he can make small chaos into big chaos very quickly. He is very good to have around when there is chaos because he is never scared and he always does the right thing if he remembers to. He is not so good to have around when there is not chaos because he tends to make chaos happen.

Dad: Most people start thinking about things from what they'd like to be happening, instead of what is actually happening. This makes them unhappy because what is actually happening is almost never exactly what you want to be happening. Dad doesn't do that. Dad starts with what actually is happening, and goes from there. Dad doesn't actually like chaos. I think he would rather there wasn't quite as much of it as there is in our lives. But he doesn't waste time thinking about that. Instead, he looks at the chaos and decides what he can do about it.

Granny: I'm going to tell you all about Granny in this story, so you don't really need to know anything now, except that it is her birthday party, and that she is trying to escape from it.

Grandad: Well, with Grandad, you'll just have to wait and see. That's the problem with introductions. Sometimes, things are too complicated for introductions. And sometimes, there are just too many beginnings, and you don't know which one to start from.

Chapter 3

Mr. Johnny Chuckles is not the right person to be in charge of a birthday party for a granny. He told us that he runs children's parties as well, but I will never let him run one of mine, and I don't think you should let him run yours either. I didn't mention Mr. Johnny Chuckles in Chapter 2, because he's not part of our family, and also he's not in the story very much (although he is in it quite a bit more than you will think he should be).

The party was in a big room in the place where Granny lives (it's like a hotel, but just for old people). In the corner, all the food was laid out with clingfilm over it, and even the birthday cake was right there in front of everyone. Nobody was looking at it except Adam and me. The cake was right there, and nobody was even looking! Grown-up parties are not like real parties at all. In a real party, you have to hide all the food, right up until it's time to eat it, otherwise nobody can even think about anything else. And that goes double for the cake. But here, the cake was right there for everyone to see, and nobody was looking. Nobody except Adam.

All the chairs in the room were orange armchairs, but they were all around the outside of the room, facing in, so instead of looking at the person they were talking to, all the old people (and there were a lot of them) had to look into the middle of the room where there was nothing except me and Adam, playing. It made us feel a bit like we should be doing some tricks, and Adam was just about to start when Mr. Johnny Chuckles came in. He stood right in the middle of the room and held up his hands for quiet.

Everyone ignored him.

Then he asked if everyone was ready to have fun. Nobody said they were because most of them didn't hear him. Those who did just kept talking to each other - which is rude when children do it, but nobody tells old people off for it. But Mr. Johnny wasn't going to give up. He had brought with him a small microphone and the biggest loudspeakers I have ever seen. They were about twice as tall as me and looked like they were probably best for a teenage party, rather than a granny's party.

Mr. Johnny Chuckles switched on his microphone and he started to speak. The first "H" in his first word (which was probably "hello,") came out of the speakers, and then just stretched out into this echoey whine, which just kept getting louder, and louder, and louder, until we couldn't hear anything but this deafening sound.

"What was that?" I asked Granny.

"It's called feedback," said Granny, ""When you put a microphone next to a speaker, any tiny sound you make gets made louder by the speaker, then the microphone picks it up and sends it to the speaker even louder, and then the microphone picks it up louder and sends it to the speaker even louder than before. So, whatever tiny sound you make just goes round, and round, and round in circles, getting louder, and louder."

The sound slowly died away. Granny said, "The same thing happens with the way people think sometimes. They get stuck in a loop that just gets bigger, and louder, and nastier." I didn't know what she meant at the time. I know now, though.

Mr. Johnny Chuckles acted as though everyone had cheered, and said, "Are we ready for some party games?" The sound was so loud, I had to cover my ears, and all the grannies slowly quietened down.

The people in charge of the place where Granny lived had brought in Mr. Johnny to organise Granny's party. It certainly hadn't been Dad's idea. When they had told Dad about it, he had said, "That's a lovely idea!" but that's Dad's way of saying, "I really don't want this to happen, but I know it's going to happen anyway."

When I told him I had worked out how to redecorate my bedroom really quickly, using only a can of paint and a hand grenade, he said, "That's a lovely idea!" Dad also says, "You have to choose your battles," but that's not my experience of battles.

Anyway, Dad had said he wouldn't come to the party. Instead, he'd said he would leave us at the party, and then pick us and Granny up afterwards, so we could all go to the Science Museum, and have ice cream.

Dad was right. Mr Johnny was not a very good choice. He made everyone be quiet, and then he made them play games and sing songs from World War Two. I watched Granny for a while. The songs didn't seem to be the sort of songs Granny likes.

Granny likes mainly punk and techno.

She looked a bit sad for a moment, then she looked round. Mr. Johnny kept saying things like, "You'll love this one!" and, "Everybody has to join in." Then Granny started smiling and joining in, singing songs and playing games, with everyone else. It looked like she was having a nice time, but I knew what she was really doing. She was Acting Normal. Nobody should have to Act Normal on their birthday.

Everything Mr. Johnny did was about rules. He knew how to make people be quiet, and make them do what he said, and he said he knew a lot of things about what other people wanted. He also said he knew how to have fun, but it was sort of headmastery fun. Fun with rules. The sort of fun where you know exactly where the edges of the fun are. Fun in a box.

I don't like fun in a box, and neither does Adam, so we crept out while everyone was singing, to find something else to do. I stopped at the door, and looked at Granny. She smiled at me, and I signalled for her to follow us, but she just went back to singing.

Everybody was following Mr. Johnny's lead. Even if people were not enjoying it, he had a way of making them try to, so I supposed that was good, because, sometimes, when you start by just going along with something, you end up enjoying it in the end. I decided Mr. Johnny would make a better headmaster than a party organiser. In fact, I decided, he would probably be very good at that, if he stopped trying to be fun all the time, and just concentrated on teaching people to enjoy things they didn't start off enjoying.

Adam and I crept along the corridor away from the party. Most of the doors were locked, but two of them were open and, luckily, one was an office (the other one was a kitchen but it was no good because all the food was in the party room being guarded). I like offices because offices have computers, and if there's one thing I really like, it's coding.

And it so happened that I had a really good idea of something I wanted to code for another party...

Chapter 4

My friend Alison is a very girly girl. She likes pink and glitter. I like pink and glitter too, but if you talked to Alison, you would think there were no other colours and nothing in the world that wasn't glittery. You should see her bedroom.

Alison even has glittery fingernails. I couldn't have glittery fingernails even if I wanted to, because the glitter gets into my experiments, and it makes electronics go all angry, and if it gets into my microscope, it makes me think I have discovered space jewels, when I have really just discovered glitter. It is also hard to climb trees with glittery fingernails, because you end up worrying about your fingernails, instead of worrying about the dinosaur chasing you.

And Alison likes fairies and ponies and unicorns (which are a kind of fairy pony) and - well, you get the idea. I don't like fairies. The tooth fairy, for example - what does she want with all those teeth? Nothing good, I'm sure. I mean, what could you eat with a million tiny baby teeth? I don't even want to think. And where does she get the money from? She must be very rich and have lots of teeth, which is a bit scary if you think about it.

If you read old stories about fairies, they're a lot less nice than the ones in new stories. And now I like them less than I ever did before. If you ever see a fairy - especially a Magic Fairy - you

17

should run away very fast, and definitely don't let it tell you what to do - but more about that later. Right now we're talking about Alison and her birthday.

Alison's birthday party was the next week, and because she is so girly, and pink, and not at all like me, it's really hard for me to think of what she wants. I go into a shop and see a million sparkly pink things, and I don't know which ones she would like (Alison is VERY fussy about the things she likes and the things she doesn't - and I can't tell the difference).

It was the same problem with Granny. I don't really understand the things Granny likes either, and I couldn't think of what to get her, so eventually I got her something that smelled of lavender - which seemed wrong, because Granny used to be a research scientist, so if she wanted something that smelled of lavender, she could genetically engineer it. I can't do presents. Christmas is a very difficult time for me.

What I can do is coding. Coding is making instructions for computers to tell them to do things you can't do yourself. There are lots of websites that let you do it, and it works like this:

You have a space on the screen where you make your code, and lots of blocks you can drag in to tell the computer what to do. If you're coding a game, you might have a "MAKE A MAZE" block and a "USE THE MOUSE TO MOVE" block. Then you link them together to make a game.

Here's a more difficult one. See if you can work out what this does:

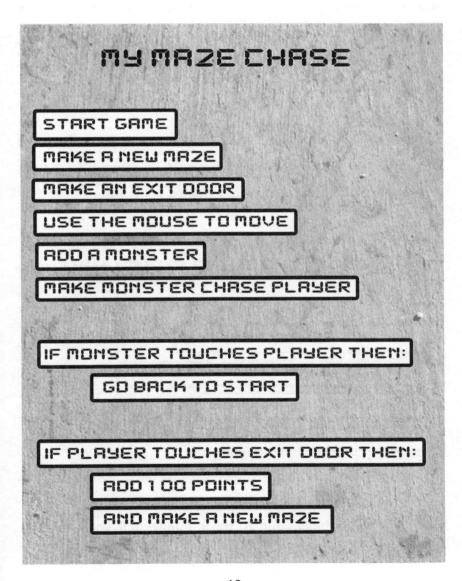

Can you guess what this code would do? Why don't you play the game in your head, later?

I got onto the computer in the office (there was a password, but it was written on a yellow Post-It Note stuck to the screen, so that was easy), and I found the coding website. Adam decided to play with the photocopier. He copied some papers, and some Lego, and his bottom.

I started to code, but I didn't want to code a maze game. I wanted to code a machine for choosing presents for people. Christmas was coming, and I needed a plan. I wanted to do this:

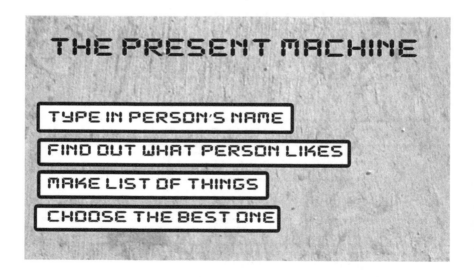

THE PRESENT MACHINE

TYPE IN PERSON'S NAME

FIND OUT WHAT PERSON LIKES

MAKE LIST OF THINGS

CHOOSE THE BEST ONE

But there aren't blocks for all those things, and you can't just invent them, so I started with this:

THE PRESENT MACHINE

ASK THE INTERNET:

"WHAT DO BOYS AND GIRLS WANT?"

LEARN

MAKE A LIST

It wasn't a finished program, but it was a start. My Present Machine could go out on the internet now, and learn about what boys and girls wanted, and make it into a list. But I needed to think more about how it could use its list to narrow the choice down to just one thing.

But by now, Adam had made a lot of photocopies of his bottom. He had put them in amongst all the papers on the desk and all over the walls and on the floor, so I decided to stop for a minute, and take them down.

While I was taking them down, Adam started looking at my program. He added a "LOOP" block. Loops are where you tell the computer to keep going round and round through some of the blocks and do the same thing over and over again. Loops are good for doing the same thing over and over, but they're also dangerous because they're a bit like the "feedback" that came from Mr. Johnny's speaker. You can end up with too much or too many things that you can't stop, getting bigger, and bigger, and bigger. If you put an "ADD AN ENEMY" block in and then put it in a loop, you can guess what happens. Suddenly you've got more, and more, and more enemies until you don't know what to do with them all. Adam likes loops, though, because chaos is his favourite thing.

I should have checked what Adam had done because it was quite accidentally clever, but not a good idea. Adam is so good at "accidentally clever" that I often think it's not an accident. I often think his brain just works in a different way from mine. You see, I usually think about something, and then think another step on, and another step on from that, until I get to the answer I want. Adam just thinks about the thing he wants and doesn't bother with the steps in the middle. He also doesn't bother thinking what will happen after he gets the answer he wants, which might be why his ideas end up with chaos so often.

Adam's loop took the list the code had learned out of things people like, and looped it back into learning again from it, and making another list, and then looping back again and again... This won't make much sense now, but later, it will.

Anyway, just as I finished clearing away all the Adam bottom pictures I could see, Granny crept into the office. I quickly stuffed all the pictures into the dustbin.

"Mr. Johnny Chuckles has got everyone playing bingo," she said. "I don't like bingo. I like dodgeball, so I dodged it."

"You escaped from your own birthday party?" I said. "Won't they miss you?"

"They seem to be having lots of fun without me. I thought I might have more fun here," said Granny. "Now, what are you up to?"

Chapter 5

"I'm doing some coding," I said. Granny smiled, but we could both see that Adam wasn't in the mood for sitting down and coding. He was looking around for something to play with and absolutely everything else in the office was especially designed not to be fun.

"Maybe we can all play," said Granny. "I've got a present for you." Granny pulled a bottle out of her pocket. It was full of black powder.

"What is it?" I asked. Granny explained that it was magnetic powder. Adam said it didn't look like much of a present, but I like experiments, and any experiment becomes automatically more fun when it has magnets in it. Granny told Adam to go into the kitchens and "borrow" some cooking oil. She said "borrow" in that special way that makes it sound like "steal", so Adam crept off.

"Now, does this computer have speakers?" she said. I looked around. It did. They were only small, but Granny put them on the desk facing each other. "Speakers have got magnets in them," she said. "They make sounds by turning the magnets on and off very fast."

I was just showing her which coding blocks make which noises when I heard Adam coming. I had thought he would bring a little bottle of oil, but he didn't. Adam was standing on top of a huge can of oil. It was bigger than he was, and he was running along on top of it to roll it down the corridor. One of the old ladies from the party was hurrying to the toilet and Adam very nearly rolled over her, like a steamroller, but luckily he turned just in time and rolled into the office.

Granny said, "We'll only need a drop," and she opened the can, and caught a little bit of oil in a tea mug. "Now watch," she said, and dropped a tiny bit of the magnetic powder into the oil, and mixed it with a spoon.

It looked like black coffee, only too thick and sticky to drink, but it didn't do anything. Adam looked disappointed. Then, Granny poured the thick liquid onto the desk between the two speakers.

It still didn't do anything.

Then, she turned on the code. The computer made a loud beeping noise, and instantly, the little blob of liquid turned spiky like a hedgehog. Tiny black shiny spikes sprung out and rippled round it as if it was a little spiny sea creature.

"What is it?" I said.

"Watch," said Granny, and she changed the code a little bit. The computer made a noise like a fart if a fart lasted for a whole minute. The spiky blob turned inside out and stood up straight like an upside-down, lumpy, black ice cream.

"What's happening?" I said.

"What do you think is happening?" said Granny. Granny always did this - I always learned a lot from Granny, but she never told me anything. She just asked me questions and let me learn what I already knew by answering them. I looked at the blob. The farting sound was still going on and it was like the blob was dancing to it.

"You said the dust was magnetic," I said.

"Yes," said Granny.

"And the speakers are magnets too," I said.

"And sound makes things shake, doesn't it?" said Granny,

"So the speakers are controlling the blob," I said. Granny smiled. "And different sounds make different shapes?"

I looked at the code on the screen and at the dancing farting blob, and I had an idea. Thinking back, it was probably a bad idea, but I don't know because it wasn't bad on its own - it needed lots of other ideas added to it before it became bad. It needed my brother's ideas, and some of Mr. Johnny Chuckle's ideas, and some of Granny's ideas. It even needed some ideas from all the children in the world, if I really think about it. Perhaps ideas are like that sometimes. Perhaps you can have a whole string of good ideas, and somehow, if you don't watch out, they can suddenly be bad when they all add together.

Anyway, it wasn't a bad idea at this bit. It was a fun idea. I just linked the "SOUND" code block to the "LEARN" code block I already had for the Present Machine, and I put in a "WEBCAM" code block so the computer could see what the blob looked like.

Now, the sound started to change. The fart became lower, and then higher. The blob stretched out into a long spiky line, then curled up into a wobbly ball. And the computer watched and learned what sounds made different shapes. Then, suddenly, the sound went all high like a whistle, and the blob leapt up into the air and spun around like a little black star. Then the sound changed again to the sort of noise a piano makes when you drop it out of a hot-air balloon (I've only ever had to do that once, but it did stop us from crashing into Big Ben).

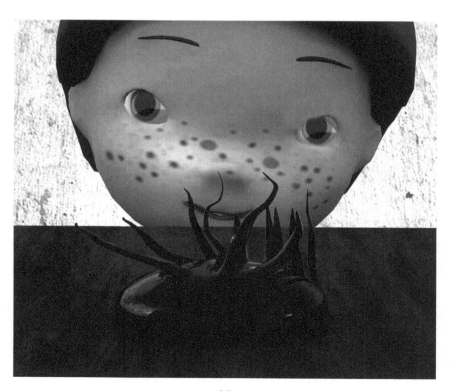

The blob loved that sound and little black arms snaked out of its sides, and it started to dance a strange, crazy dance. Granny and Adam were laughing and clapping. This was so much better than playing bingo.

"Mr. Johnny has got bigger speakers," said Adam, suddenly. And I should have stopped right there, and remembered the way my brother's mind worked, but I was distracted because then Granny smiled, and said, "Do you call those speakers? I was once at a party where there were speakers you could live in!"

And Granny started to tell me a story about the biggest and best party she ever went to - maybe the biggest and best party anybody in the world ever went to.

"Stop talking," I said, and I turned back to the computer code.

Chapter 6

Granny looked sad. She thought I had said stop because I didn't want to hear about her party, but that wasn't it. I said stop because Granny's stories are so good I like to write them down, and I can't write very fast, so I stopped the dancing blob code, and the noise, and I dragged a "RECORD" block and a "TYPE" block into my program. Now the computer was recording and remembering Granny's story so I could have it later.

"Start again," I said, and she started talking. This is exactly what she said (see, it works). I've put it all in here because it explains why Granny doesn't have a Grandad to go with her:

"I was once at a party where there were speakers so big you could live in them. You wouldn't, though, because they were loud enough to break windows. They had to be that big because this wasn't just any ordinary party. This was the biggest party in the world, and it was on a farm in America. There were about half a million people at this party.

"It was a very different time from now - and I loved it because it felt like everyone was doing experiments, and, well, you know how much I like experiments.

"Lots of people were growing their own food, and making their own clothes, and they were all wondering if people really needed to have wars and things like that."

I said that I often wondered about that too, but Granny told me that this was a time when everyone was thinking about wars especially much, because lots of countries were pointing really big bombs at each other and wondering if the other one was going to drop bombs on them, and whether they should get in first with their bombs, so it was all a bit scary, and all the armies were watching everything that happened in the sky and hoping it wasn't a bomb on the way to blow them up (I shortened that bit, but I put it in, because it was important because of what Granny said later).

"Anyway," said Granny, "every musician I had ever heard of was performing at the party, and when I arrived, there were just thousands of people, all dressed in coloured clothes, and waving banners and having fun. And you could hear the speakers all the way at the other side of the field, and I thought that was amazing, so I wanted to know how they worked. I pushed my way through all the people, and all the mud (there was a lot of mud) until I got right to the front. By then, the music was so loud, it was making my hair dance all on its own. I looked up at these giant speakers and that was when I saw him.

"He was standing on top of the biggest speaker, dancing like a strange, wild creature. When he came down, I saw he had a toolbox with him. I asked what it was, and he told me it was his job to build the giant speakers. He explained to me how they worked, and I told him I was really interested in the way things worked.

"He told me his name was Anton, and that he really wanted to be a toymaker. Later, we went back to his tent and he showed me the designs of the toys he wanted to make. They were mad. Strange, insane toys. Electronic and mechanical toys you couldn't believe could ever exist. There were flying dragons that really flew, on paper wings, and dolls that talked and listened to you. And huge, robot arms you could control with your real arms, and giant fishing net scoops, which could blow a thousand bubbles at a time when you waved them in the air. They were the most amazing, impossible toys you could ever imagine. But, of course, none of them were built - they were just designs.

"Then I told him about some of my experiments, and the things that I had made with chemicals. I told him I did a lot of crystal growing. We got on really well together, and we were both interested in the same kinds of experiments and inventions. We decided that we would work together on our experiments, and make great inventions of our own. And the other thing we promised each other was that we would never, ever give those inventions to the army, because the army already had enough dangerous inventions, and the world did not need any more of those.

"That night, we decided to do some experiments. I grew some special crystals, and we wired them into the stage lights. In the morning, when the music started, we planned it so that the lights would reflect through the crystals into lasers, and there would be the greatest light show ever.

"And there was - sort of. The thing was, I don't think either of us knew quite how well our experiment would work. It lit up the whole sky with lasers which made the coloured shapes of strange aeroplanes reflected on the clouds. The speakers thundered so hard, it shook the ground like a thousand explosions. The crowd loved it!

"Or, at least, they loved it until the real army planes came to see what was going on. Then they started running. Suddenly, half a million people were all running in different directions and the reflections on the clouds looked like enemy planes, and the speakers sounded like a war had started, so you can guess what the army thought, and they all got their bombs and missiles ready to fire at all the other countries they thought were attacking them.

"We didn't actually cause a world war that day, but it was pretty close, and in the confusion, your grandfather and I got separated."

"And you didn't find him again?" I said. Granny looked sad.

"Actually, I did," she said, "when everything calmed down, I saw him. He was on the other side of the field, talking to one of the men from the army. He was showing the man the designs for our light show. But, remember, we had both made a promise to each other, that whatever happened, whatever experiments and inventions we came up with, we would never, ever show them to the army, just in case they decided to use them.

"When I saw what he was doing, I grabbed one of the lights and pointed it through one of my crystals so that it burnt the designs right out of his hands. He turned to look at me, and I just stared at him from the other side of the field, and then I ran away. That was the last time I ever saw him.

"When I found out that I was pregnant with your dad, I didn't try to find Anton. Part of me was still angry, but the other part knew I should keep away. Your grandfather wasn't the sort of person to look after a child. He was a beautiful kind of crazy, and he needed to do his own, mad inventions - having children would have just got in his way."

I looked at Granny. She was staring off out of the window with a sad look in her eyes. "But," I said, "that's how you must have looked to him - like a crazy experimenter." Granny thought for a moment. Then she shook her head.

"Doesn't matter now, I don't suppose. It's all in the past," she said. But it wasn't all in the past, and it did matter. Otherwise, I would have left it out of the story, wouldn't I?

The recording block worked well, but I forgot that I'd made it part of my Present Machine code. That's another thing that doesn't really matter right now - but will matter later, so you should probably remember it.

Anyway, I got so caught up with Granny's story that I didn't see Adam go. He had got a bit bored, I think. Adam doesn't like listening to people talk, even if they're telling him really interesting or important things. If you have something to say to Adam, always say it at the beginning of the sentence. For example, say:

"Don't run into that field because there are dinosaurs there!"

Don't say:

"That field is full of dinosaurs. If you run into that field, you might be eaten by them," because Adam will only hear, "that field is full of dinosaurs - run into that field," before he starts running into the field.

Anyway, he had gone, and I thought at first that he might have gone to take the giant oil can back to the kitchen, but then I noticed that the rest of Granny's bottle of magnetic powder was gone from the table as well. And that was when I knew that a bit of chaos was coming.

Chapter 7

I didn't have time to say anything, though, because, at that second, the door opened. Mr. Johnny Chuckles was standing there. He looked sad. The sort of disappointed-angry-sad that teachers get when you've broken something, or accidentally opened a portal to another dimension (I only did that once, but really, it would have been better if I had never done it - or better for the library, anyway).

"We're playing bingo!" he said, as if playing bingo was the only thing anyone in the world could possibly want to do.

"We're playing with magnets," I said. Mr. Johnny Chuckles looked at the black splodge on the desk, then at Granny and me.

"You'd enjoy bingo more," he said.

"I don't think we would," said Granny. Mr. Johnny looked at her as though she had said something impossible.

"Of course you would," said Mr. Johnny. "I've read lots of books about old people, and I have designed the best old people party ever!" He pulled a big wad of paper out of his pocket, "Look!" He said. The paper had lots of graphs and writing on it. He started reading:

"68% of old people like bingo. 72% enjoy singing songs. Look - only 5% like playing with magnets!" He pointed at the graphs. "My party has been carefully planned to have everything you could ever want. Do you want to see my cake/tea fraction calculations? They're the most accurate in the world!"

"No, dear," said Granny, "I don't want to see them. I'm playing with my granddaughter."

It was like when someone came to our school saying they wanted to get more girls interested in football. And they gave us pink whistles and put perfume in the changing rooms, and gave the older girls Twitter breaks in the middle of matches. It didn't make more girls interested in football. It just made the girls who were already interested in football annoyed because all they wanted was to play football. It's not really about giving people what you think they want all the time. It's about giving them everything there is and letting them pick.

I was about to say this to Mr. Johnny, but then I saw his disappointed-sad expression change to a real, properly sad expression. His bottom lip stuck out, and his shoulders and eyebrows sloped down, and his eyes filled up with tears.

"All I ever wanted was to give people what they wanted!" he wailed. "I made the perfect party! Why don't you like it?" He sank down into a chair, put his hands over his eyes, and started to sob.

I started to feel sorry for Mr. Johnny, and I was just about to tell him it was all OK when the office door burst open, and Adam ran in, laughing. It was Adam's special laugh. The one he saves for when he has made a really big bit of chaos. Suddenly, I couldn't say it was all OK because I knew that it was very much not all OK.

From the other room, there was a loud roar that made the whole floor shake. The door of the party room flew open and old people started rushing out as fast as their Zimmer frames and wheelchairs could carry them. The sound in the room behind them started to change. it went high, and then it went low, and then it went sort of grumbly and clangy, like a thousand pianos falling out of a thousand hot-air balloons, and crashing their way down the side of a thousand, extra big, Big Bens.

"What have you done?" I said to Adam, but it was a silly question. I knew what Adam had done. It was really very obvious what Adam had done. Adam's face, the missing magnet powder, the loud noise from Mr. Johnny's speakers, the giant can of oil. It was really very obvious.

40

"Come on," said Mr. Johnny, "we have to finish the bingo!" He suddenly got up and started trying to push Granny and me back towards the party room.

"Can't you see what's happening?" I said. "There's a magnet monster in there!" But Mr. Johnny wasn't listening. He wasn't thinking right. I've noticed grown-ups do that sometimes when strange things happen. They can't work out what to do, so they just try to do whatever they were doing before only louder and stronger - as if they think that doing their old plans will make all the new things just go away. It never works, but grown-ups do it a lot if you watch them.

I thought very quickly. Adam must have made a giant magnet monster, and used the giant speakers in the party room to control it. Mr. Johnny was playing music with a laptop, and that was connected to the WI-FI - so Adam had probably signed into my code to make it all work. And that meant my little, learning, noise-making, magnetic monster program could also control Adam's giant, learning, noise-making, magnetic monster. And, by the sounds coming from the party room, it was learning very fast.

And an old people's home is a very bad place for a giant, magnetic monster.

I decided it would be best to run. I looked at Granny, and I could see she was thinking exactly the same as me. We pushed Mr. Johnny back into his chair, and I grabbed Adam, and we ran out of the office. I thought it was best to lock Mr. Johnny in, to protect him and us, so I locked the office door from the outside.

Thinking back, it was probably not a good idea to take a man who really, really wanted to give people what they wanted, but didn't really understand what that was, and lock him in a room with a computer code that searched the internet for everything boys and girls wanted, and kept learning and looping forever. Still, I wasn't really thinking back at the time. At the time, I was thinking mainly forward, about the giant, magnetic monster.

"Look!" shouted Adam, giggling. We looked, and big, black tentacles were jumping and spiking out of the door to the party room, in time with the farting, whooping, clanging noises coming from the speakers. The spikes were learning. They shot out and touched the wall, then shrank back. Then they shot out again, and, this time, they made a big crack in the wall. The sound went all low and squelchy, like someone jumping in and out of a box of whoopee cushions, and the tentacle curled around the door, and slowly pushed it open.

"Come on!" I said, and I pulled Granny and Adam away from the door. We ran down the corridor, with the tentacle wobbling and smashing behind us, and ducked into the kitchen. Through the door, I could just see the magnet monster, flowing out of the party room after us. It was huge and shiny and black, and its body kept changing shape. Little spikes and big spikes, and ripples and waves jumped up and flowed around it, giving it arms, and legs, and tentacles whenever it needed them, to crawl, and drag, and bubble towards the kitchen. On top of the monster, it was carrying Mr. Johnny Chuckles' laptop, and it was pointing the laptop's camera in front of it.

"Interesting," said Granny. "It needs the camera to see where it's going."

Everybody from the party was still trying to escape down the corridor. The monster couldn't move very fast, but neither could they, so it was like a slow-motion race between the old people and the splotchy monster.

In a kids party, when people are running around screaming, it's a sign that the party is going well. When it happens in an old people's party, people tend to think it's going badly. This party was definitely going badly.

"We need to unplug the speakers," I said.

44

Granny nodded. "But the speakers are in the party room, and we can't get past the monster."

"We could zap it with a laser!" said Adam. Adam's plans often involve zapping things, but also, they often miss out important bits - like not having a laser.

"The monster is made of oil," said Granny, "if we zap it with a laser, it will catch fire."

Adam smiled. "Goody!" he said. I decided a giant, magnetic monster was bad enough. A giant, magnetic monster on fire would probably be an even bigger problem.

"But if we pointed the laser at the camera," said Granny, "we could distract it long enough for you to run past and unplug the speakers."

That sounded like a good idea, but we still didn't have a laser. Now I've read about lasers on the internet, and you can make them with a very strong light (there was a flashlight in the kitchen) and some lenses (Granny's reading glasses would work), but I also needed a crystal to turn the ordinary light into special laser light. That was the problem. I told Granny.

"That's no problem. We'll just make a diamond," said Granny.

If you want to make diamonds at home, it's actually easy. It's a lot easier than I thought.

Things you need to make diamonds at home:
- Some leads from a pencil.
- Two coffee mugs.
- A grown-up.
- A drop of oil.
- A microwave oven.
- A kitchen which you don't mind getting on fire.

There are more instructions on the internet, but, to put it simply, you use the microwave to make the carbon from the pencil lead so hot it turns into diamond. The coffee mugs are there to stop the microwave from exploding, but they don't stop it from melting and going on fire, so it's probably best not to use your best kitchen.

The diamond you end up with isn't the kind of diamond you'd want to wear as jewellery. It's more like a dirty speck of dust.

Can you guess what the kitchen looked like after we'd made our microwave diamond?

It didn't look very good. We had a microwave oven which was very melted and smelly, and a kitchen which was very much on fire, and filling up with black smoke. We had a little speck of diamond which we'd stuck to the end of the glasses on a wire, and on the other end we had the flashlight.

The only way out of the kitchen was through the door, and on the other side of the door was a giant, magnetic monster.

One important thing to remember about new inventions is that you have to test them before you use them. This is because, often, there are problems. Often, you don't know exactly how they will work until you test them, and unexpected things can easily happen (like when I once made an army of zombie robots which took our town to pieces). Always test your experiments before you use them.

But I thought the laser, if it did work, would only work once, so we couldn't really test it before we faced the monster. I gave the laser to Granny, so she could fire it while I ducked through and turned off the speakers. While we stood at the door, waiting, I did think of a few things which could happen when I turned the laser on.

Things which could have happened:
- The laser could have just not worked, and the monster could have got us.

- The laser could have worked too well and burned a hole in the building where Granny lived.
- The laser could have been difficult to aim, and Granny could have hit the monster instead of the camera so that the monster went on fire.
- I could have been caught by the monster as I ran past it.
- The laser could have worked too well, and been difficult to aim at the same time, and it could have drilled a hole right through to the earth's core, causing all the molten rock to shoot up and destroy the world.

I thought of a few more problems too, but they were too serious to think about properly before Adam said, "Ready, Steady, Go!" And flung open the doors.

Chapter 8

As soon as Adam opened the doors, the magnet monster turned its camera to point at us and spiked and jumped forward at us. It was so big, it nearly filled the whole doorway, and sharp, pointy needles kept springing out from it in every gap. Granny lifted the laser and pointed it right at the camera, which must have been difficult because her glasses had been made into the laser. She shouted to Adam, and he turned the power on.

Instantly, there was a huge flash of light, and a red beam shot from the front of our laser, straight into the camera of the laptop it was carrying high above, what would have been its head, if it had a head. The sound changed to a high squeal, like a hundred whistles being blown by an octopus, and a big wobble went through the creature. It started thrashing about, randomly throwing out spikes, in all directions. A gap opened up between the monster and the doorframe and I saw my chance. I dived at it, and just then, the laser flickered and went out.

The laser had blinded the camera for a few seconds, but now it could see again and the noise changed back. My gap was closing, but I just managed to dive through and run off down towards the party room.

I could hear the creature turn around and start chasing me, and in front of me, the sound from the speakers got so loud, it was shaking the floor like a diplodocus on a trampoline. I ran into the room, with the creature just behind me, threw myself at the biggest speaker and pulled out the plug.

The sound stopped in a second, and there was silence. I turned around, in time to see the magnetic monster spike once more, and then suddenly turn back into sticky, black oil, which exploded over everything in the room, including all the chairs, the birthday cake and me.

The room was a complete mess, and almost everything in it was broken, oily, smelly, and slightly magnetic, and when the other old people started coming back, they didn't look happy at all. But when Granny and Adam came back in, they were giggling together, so I thought everything was probably all right.

Chapter 9

"I'm sorry I ruined your party," I said to Granny, as the white cleaning van arrived to clean up the place where Granny lived, "and I'm sorry that you and your friends won't be able to live here for a while." The cleaners started to pick their way through the rubble of broken armchairs, and strange, black, sticky splashes of magnet monster liquid. The microwave fire had made a bit of a mess of the kitchen, and there were big, burnt holes in the ceiling and the floor, but it had made all the water pipes burst, so that had put the fire out. We didn't look too closely at the kitchen, because the smell of burning, melting, flooding, and food isn't nice. Granny looked serious for a moment. Then she grinned at me.

"That was the best party I've been to in years!" she said, and she giggled one of her naughty schoolgirl giggles.

Suddenly, I remembered something.

"Mr. Johnny Chuckles!" I said. "We locked him in the office!" We opened the door, and he was sitting quietly, staring into the computer screen where my code was written. He ignored us as we came in. "Are you OK?" I said.

Mr. Johnny turned, slowly. His eyes looked quite strange, and he was staring. He spoke quietly, as if he was in a dream. "Yes, I'm fine," he said, "I'm absolutely fine."

If I had known then what I know now, I'd probably have taken a bit more notice of Mr. Johnny Chuckles right then. But if I'd known, I'd have done a lot of things differently. Instead, I just thought he was behaving in the same shocked, lost way adults behave in quite often around Adam and me, and we shut the door and went out to meet Dad.

Dad was parked in the carpark.

"Have fun?" he said.

I was about to say something, but Adam and Granny just said, "Yes!" very loudly. Dad had started the car to drive off when I saw his eyes in the mirror. He was looking at me, all covered in splashes of liquid magnet. He looked puzzled, and then I saw him look out of the window, at the burning building, and the fire engines, and the huddle of old people standing in the car park.

He paused. Then he opened his mouth to say something. Then he closed it again. He looked at Granny, then at Adam, giggling in the back seat. Then he shook his head.

"Ice cream, everybody?" said Dad, and he drove off.

Part 2:

Act Normal, And Don't Tell Anyone That Pink Is Your Enemy

Chapter 10

So, now you know about Granny, let's get back to the chase. I told you that we were running from the hospital, and the doctors were chasing us. We got out into the car park and skidded around the corner with me hanging onto the back of the super-fast wheelchair, and Adam sprinting away in front of us.

The doctors were behind, and I was pretty sure that if we got far enough away, then they would give up, but it wasn't the doctors I was worried about, it was the fairies because they could fly, which made them extra dangerous. As soon as one fairy spotted us, the rest would be after us in a second. We needed something fast, but I thought it would be best not to have something electric because the forklift trucks looked angry.

OK, hang on, this still probably doesn't make much sense to you, does it? I didn't tell you about the forklift trucks, and the fairies, did I? I think I need to go back a bit and explain about the fairies, and about why Granny was in hospital in the first place.

The bit about Granny is the easy bit, so let's do that first. Granny was in hospital because she had a fall. This is something that happens sometimes. People often say, about old people, that they, "had a fall, and now they're in hospital", but they don't say anything else, so it can be a bit confusing. Adam has a fall at least twenty times every day, and he almost never goes to hospital for more than a couple of days.

Granny's fall was when she was arguing with the man in control of the place where she had to move to, after the magnet monster problem. He had told her she couldn't play punk rock music in her room, and she was trying to show him how to dance to it when she slipped over.

Explaining about the fairies is a bit more difficult, but I suppose that bit begins with Alison's birthday party...

Chapter 11

Remember I told you how I'd coded the Present Machine to go out on the internet and learn what sort of things lots of girls and lots of boys like, because I really couldn't work them out? Well, in the end, I somehow lost the code - it had vanished from my coding account by the time I got home, so I had to just go out and buy something for Alison's birthday party.

I nearly got a microscope slide with some shrimp eggs on it because they were pink, but that was just me thinking, Alison would like what I like, but only pink. I went for a pink pen and pink paper in the end. The paper had glitter on, and the pen had a big pink feather sticking out of it. I would never have bought it for myself, because the feather was the wrong colour to be from any actual, specific bird, and that would have annoyed me. I mean, what did they want me to think about the feather and the bird and the pen? And why take something that's already interesting, and make it less interesting by changing its colour?

Anyway, I got it, because, even if she got bored with the pink and the glitter, she would still have a pen, and you can never have enough pens.

You see, I told you I'm not very good at presents. I'm starting to worry about all the things I'll have to buy at Christmas.

Anyway, the party was definitely not as good as Granny's party. Of course, there was a pink theme, so I had to wear pink. I have a pink dress which is much newer and cleaner than all my other clothes. It has no grass stains, or mud, or blood, or acid burns, or dinosaur poo on it. There is a reason why my pink dress is so new and clean. Can you guess the reason?

That's right. It's because I absolutely hate it.

There was a "no boys" rule, but Adam came, because he was my brother, and Dad had nowhere else to send him. He did not like it at all, and neither did I. I started to feel very much on my own, very quickly.

If you have never seen Alison's bedroom, it is amazing. Absolutely everything Alison owns is pink and furry or feathery or glittery, and most things are all three at the same time. A whole flock of flamingos could hide in Alison's bedroom, and you wouldn't even know they were there.

Also, if you took all the Queen's jewels into Alison's bedroom, they would actually make the place look LESS glittery. This was new. Alison was always a bit of a pink girl, and she would always go pink if she had the chance, but now she seemed to have gone totally crazy with it.

Anyway, I said I started to feel on my own. All the other girls were being strange. When I arrived, Alison was sitting with everyone else around her. They were all sitting in complete silence, and they were all reading.

"What are you reading?" I said.

Alison looked up, "We are reading the Magic Fairy books," she said.

"Magic Fairies," said everyone else, all at the same time without looking up.

"What are they?" I said.

"Haven't you heard of the Magic Fairy books?" said Alison.

"Magic Fairies," said everyone else without looking up. It was WeirdNormal - that's my word for when things are weird, but at the same time, everyone is doing them, so they are normal.

Like everyone staring at a TV when all that's on is something they've all seen a hundred times before, or always wearing training shoes and tracksuits, but never doing any exercise. If you think about it for long enough, almost everything people do is WeirdNormal.

"You should read Magic Fairies," said Alison.

"Magic Fairies," said everyone else.

I sat in the corner for a while looking at all the pink things. I was feeling quite lonely, actually, and I could see Adam was starting to get a bit bored, which is always a danger sign that he is about to start chaos.

"What did you get for your birthday?" I said. I didn't really want to know, but it was better than just sitting quietly, in the corner of the pink room, in my pink dress, feeling sad.

"Money," said Alison.

"What are you going to do with the money?" I said.

"Buy Magic Fairy dolls," she said.

"Buy Magic Fairy dolls," the rest all said, at the same time, "we must buy Magic Fairy dolls."

"What are they?" I said.

Alison looked at me as though she couldn't believe I didn't already know. "You read about them in the Magic Fairy books."

"Magic Fairies," said everyone else.

I started to feel very much as though Alison was not being my friend any more. In fact, it felt like all of my friends at the party were not being my friends any more. This was bad, and I really didn't understand what was going on.

The rest of the party was horrible. Horrible and quiet and pink, and lonely. When Dad put us in the car on the way home, he said, "How was the party?"

Adam said, "It was rubbish!" But, I just burst into tears.

When we got home, we looked in the party bags. I bet you can guess what they had in them.

Yes, it was a Magic Fairies book. I started to wish I hadn't worried so much about not getting Alison something I liked instead of something she liked. Giving me a Magic Fairies book was exactly like me giving her shrimp eggs on a microscope slide. What would I want with a Magic Fairies book? What did that have to do with me? (Quite a lot, actually, as it happened, but I didn't know that then.)

I threw the book into the corner of my bedroom without even opening it. It would probably have saved time if I had read it there and then, though.

Adam didn't have a Magic Fairies book in his party bag. He had a different book. Exactly the same size and shape, but on his it said "Tank Monsters" instead of "Magic Fairies". This was obviously the "boy" version. As if all boys had to like Tank Monsters and all girls had to like Magic Fairies.

Actually, as it happened, it was OK for Adam. Adam is that kind of boy, and tanks and monsters are two of his favourite things.

Chapter 12

If the party was WeirdNormal, then school the next day was doublespookycreepyweirdnormal. That's not even something I thought I would ever need a word for, and I'm somebody who once woke up with a thousand rhinos in her garden!

When Dad dropped us off in the playground, I noticed straight away that something was wrong. It was not the end of the world.

You know when you watch a film, with the end of the world in it, and you see everyone running, screaming in all directions, and broken things lying everywhere, and some people chasing each other, and other people crying, and some people acting completely mad, or being zombies?

Well, the playground wasn't at all like that. Which was odd. Because normally, it's exactly like that.

Normally, all the girls and all the boys are playing, and running and shouting together. There are often some groups of girls talking about things that most boys aren't interested in and there are usually some groups of boys playing in the mud by the tree where most of the girls don't like to go, but today it was different.

Today, ALL the girls were sitting on one side of the playground, reading Magic Fairies books, and ALL the boys were sitting on the other side reading Tank Monsters books.

Whenever anyone looked up from their book, they looked across at Adam and me, standing in the middle of the playground, as though we were doing something wrong, by just standing there, not reading.

It felt really odd, and a bit scary. Normally, I like reading, but this was a bit too much. I was glad when the bell rang, but all through lessons people were sneakily reading under their desks and whispering to each other things I couldn't hear. Every time anyone looked up at me, they looked strange - as though me NOT reading a Magic Fairies book was the strange thing. It felt like there was some big plan going on in the world and I was the only one who didn't know all about it.

Lunchtime was even stranger…

Chapter 13

At lunchtime, they had to cancel school. Cancelling school is a really big deal, and it only ever happens when something really serious is going on. Like when the cheetah escaped, or when the zombie robots attacked, or when they thought there were aliens (there actually was only one alien, but I made everyone think there were loads so that the one alien could escape - but that's in another story).

Anyway, the teachers phoned all the parents and they all came to drag their children away. The children wanted to stay and fight, but the parents dragged them out anyway. The dinner hall was a complete mess, and it was a lot like the end of the world (but not in a good way like normal playtime).

A lot of teachers and parents asked me if it was my fault that the fight started, but I just Acted Normal. In fact, it wasn't my fault this time. I really was Normal - it was just everyone else who wasn't.

To be fair, people were probably right to ask if it was my fault. Are you good with chance fractions? Like when you roll a dice, the chance of getting a 6 is 1/6th because there are 6 numbers, and only 1 of them is a 6.

School has been cancelled 10 times this year, and 9 times it has been my fault. That's a fraction of 9/10 which is very nearly 1. A chance of 1 means ABSOLUTELY DEFINITELY, so it was worth asking me.

The fight started in the dinner hall. The hall was quiet because everyone was reading, at their tables, while their lunch got slowly cold in front of them. I was in the queue with Adam, in between Alison and Alfred, and we had just got to the front. Because they had to hold their trays, it was the only time in the whole day they weren't reading Magic Fairies and Tank Monsters books.

It was my only chance to find out more about this mystery, so I asked Alfred about Tank Monsters and he started going on about how great they were. It wasn't getting me anywhere, so I stopped him, and asked about Magic Fairies instead.

"Eughrrr!" said Alfred. "They're rubbish!"

Adam was listening, and he immediately turned to Alison, and said, "Alfred says Magic Fairies are rubbish!"

About four girls in the queue next to Alison heard this, and they all shouted, "Tank Monsters are stupid!"

From there, it was about 15 seconds between the quietest lunchtime I have ever seen in my life to utter, screaming, food-throwing, baked-beans-on-the-floor, hair-pulling, cake-face-squashing, table-tipping chaos. This, I think, is a new record for Adam. Everybody in the whole hall was fighting everybody else. Boys against girls. Girls against boys. Though very quickly you couldn't tell which was which because everyone was covered in baked beans, custard, sponge cake, and ratatouille.

The fight spread out into the playground, and pretty soon the whole school was fighting. All except me and Adam. We went and hid in the library until Dad came to pick us up. The library was my choice. I knew it would be the only place which didn't have Magic Fairies or Tank Monsters books in it. Mrs. Flooch, the Librarian, had refused to keep them.

While we were waiting, and watching the teachers trying to stop the fighting in the playground, I asked her why, and she shrugged. "I can't see the appeal," she said, "there's nothing much to them."

"People seem to like them," I said.

"It's just a fad. It'll be over in a week, and they'll be onto something else," she said. But I remember Mrs. Flooch also said that about Harry Potter. Mrs. Flooch's idea of what children should like reading is probably one of the reasons the library is so empty most of the time.

When Dad came to pick us up, he just looked around the playground at the food-covered, fighting children.

"You two look clean," he said.

"We weren't part of it," I said.

"Are you sure there's nothing going on?" said Dad.

I wanted to tell him that there was, but I knew that his next question would be "What?" and I wouldn't be able to answer because I didn't have a clue.

Chapter 14

It was going to be a few days until the school could be opened again, so I decided to do a bit of investigation. I got the two party bags and opened them. I had been given "Magic Fairies: The Baby Unicorn", and Adam had got "Tank Monsters: The Robot Werewolf". The two books looked completely different, but at the bottom of the cover, the author's name was the same: JC & PM Both series of books were by the same people.

I decided to read some of each book, but I guessed something in the books had made all the kids at school go WeirdNormal, and I did not want to end up like that, so I put a timer on myself and only read one paragraph from one book, and then a paragraph from the other. It would be a bit confusing, but I hoped that would stop me from getting hooked into the books.

I'm going to show you the first bit of, "Magic Fairies: The Baby Unicorn", But I think it's dangerous, so I'm doing what grownups do with secret and dangerous writing. It's called "redacting"

73

"It was a bright and sunny day on Magic Fairy Island, and all the ▮▮ *fairies were skipping and playing. Everybody loves Magic* ▮▮▮ *and* ▮▮▮▮ *wants more Magic Fairy toys. You should go out and buy a Magic Fairy toy from the Magic Faries' range right now. All the flowers were* ▮▮▮*, and the grass was pink, and all the clouds in the sky* ▮▮ *pink too* ▮▮▮▮ *everybody loves pink.*

"Suddenly, Mary the Fairy met a lovely baby unicorn. It ▮▮ *big round eyes and a smiley face. The unicorn told Mary* ▮▮ *those horrible Tank Monsters, on Tank Monster Island, were* ▮▮▮ *naughty again, and all the Magic Fairies had to* ▮▮ *them."*

It went on like that for quite a long time, and I wanted to read more, but I was starting to feel a bit dizzy, and I knew I had to read some of Tank Monsters as well, so I stopped. Here is the first bit of "Tank Monsters: The robot werewolf". I've redacted this as well, for your safety. Do you spot anything weird?

"It was a dark and stormy night on Tank Monster Island, and ▮▮ *the scary monsters* ▮▮▮ *shouting and fighting. Everybody loves Tank Monsters, and* ▮▮▮▮ *wants more Tank Monster toys. You should go out and buy a Tank* ▮▮▮ *toy from the Tank Monsters range right now. All the bombs were exploding, and the houses were exploding, and all the rockets in the sky were exploding too because everybody loves explosions.*

"Suddenly, Frank the Tank met a scary robot werewolf. It ██ *big sharp teeth and a growly face. The werewolf told Frank that those horrible Magic Fairies on* ████ ████ *island were* ████ *naughty again, and all the Tank Monsters had to* ██ *them."*

Did you notice?

Yes, that's it! They're the same. The same exact story with some of the words changed to make one of them all girly, and one of them all boyey.

It was very puzzling. I decided to stop reading because it was all making me feel a bit strange.

That night, when Dad was tucking me in, he asked me why school had been cancelled. I tried to explain that it had something to do with the books, but I don't think I explained very well, because it didn't even make sense to me when I said it.

There were Magic Fairies and Tank Monsters in my dreams that night. I dreamt that everyone in the whole world had turned into either Magic Fairies or Tank Monsters, and they were all arguing about who was best. In my dream, I was the only person in the world who was normal, and absolutely everyone else was waiting for me to pick which side I was on. It was really confusing.

When I woke up, I really wanted to read more of the books, but they were not next to my bed. I asked Dad, and he said he had borrowed them. I asked him why, and when I could have them back, and all he said was, "Let's see what happens with the other children first, shall we?"

I was very angry with Dad for taking my books away, because I really wanted to know what happened next. But, when I started thinking about the books, I realised the other odd thing about them. Did you notice it?

Both books had bits in, where they stopped telling the story, and started telling the person reading the book to go out and buy things. They also kept saying what "everybody" likes - as if they wanted everybody to like the same things.

I wondered what would happen if you read those things over and over again, like my friends at school were. What if those instructions kept going over and over on every page, and if kids kept reading the same messages over and over again. What would happen then?

I decided to look for the writers JC & PM on the internet. There wasn't much there, but I did find out where the books were all printed, and Adam and I decided to investigate.

Chapter 15

Luckily, the place where the books were being printed was in our town. I thought that was a real surprise, because these books were being read all over the whole world, and it could have been anywhere. Now I think about it, it wasn't that surprising, and it also wasn't very lucky - but I didn't know how it all fitted together then.

Adam and I asked Dad if we could go out and play, and he said we could. Because school was cancelled and his work wasn't cancelled, he had about a thousand things going on, that all had to happen at the same time, and he was probably glad we were playing outside instead of doing experiments in the kitchen, which I told him was my other choice of what to do.

I didn't tell him that we were getting on the bus to the other side of town, to where the book company was, but I thought we'd be back before he noticed. I didn't know then that we would actually be stealing Granny, and escaping on a steam train to the other side of the world before we went home, but I think if you don't know something, you can't lie about it, can you? So, really, I should only be told off about the little thing of getting on a bus. Not all the big things that happened next.

The building where the books were made was a big factory. There was a front door and a back door. I went to the front door, but Adam wanted to go to the back because there were loads of big lorries there. I saw pretty quickly that Adam had the best idea.

The front was a little door, and behind it, there was a white room with a sofa like a doctor's waiting room and a desk with a lady behind it who was always on the phone. There were a few Magic Fairy and Tank Monster books lying around, but they were just there for show. If you wanted to have a meeting with somebody in the factory, then the front was probably the place they wanted you to go.

If you wanted to sneak around and secretly investigate what was going on at the factory, without anyone noticing you, then the big, wide, unguarded back doors, with all the lorries coming and going all the time, were a much better place to go.

I followed Adam (he's much better at sneaking because he practises it all the time). We ran towards the big doors, snuck along the side wall, and ducked into the factory. Inside, it was a huge room, filled with boxes and boxes of books. I have never seen so many books in my whole life. If you imagine the biggest bookshop you have ever seen, but all the books are packed away in boxes, and stacked from the floor to the ceiling in a massive maze, it was like that. Only you also have to imagine that instead of lots of different books like you get in a bookshop, they were ALL either Tank Monster books or Magic Fairy books. I checked some of the boxes, and there was absolutely nothing else.

There are lots of different Tank Monster and Magic Fairy books. About a hundred different ones in each series, but I didn't (luckily) have a chance to read any before a big, yellow forklift truck spun around the corner and started heading straight for us. I grabbed Adam and pulled him in between two boxes, and we watched the forklift zoom past. It had a big box on the front, and it stopped at the doors, where a big lorry was waiting, lifted the box up, and slid it into the lorry. Then it turned around and zoomed off towards us.

That was when I saw there was nobody in it. It was a robot forklift! Adam saw too, and he jumped onto the back of it as it rolled past. Adam loves anything robot. I had to follow, and the truck took us back inside the factory. We drove past a big room where the books were being packed into boxes by robot arms.

When we got to another room where huge rolls of paper, with pages and pages of writing, were being printed, and cut and shaped into books, by more robot arms, I jumped off, and Adam followed.

The robot forklift carried on to a box of books lying on the floor, picked it up, and turned back towards the rest of the factory. On the front, it had two little cameras, like little glass eyes, and for a second, as it turned, it stopped, with its eyes looking straight at us. Somewhere inside it, something whirred. I signalled to Adam to freeze (which he's not very good at) and we both stood completely still.

After a second, the forklift whirred again, and it drove away. Maybe it had spotted us. Maybe it hadn't. I looked around the room. The reels of paper spun out very fast, sheet after sheet, and page after page was being printed, sliced into pages with giant robotic knives, and stuck into book, after book, after book.

This was where the books were being printed. We stood and looked at the giant printing machine, spinning out more and more Magic Fairy books, and I realised something else. If there was a giant printer, then there had to be a computer somewhere telling it what to print.

There was a little door into a little office, and when we went through and looked at the computer screen, that was when things got a lot stranger...

Chapter 16

It was a big screen and it covered the whole wall, and around the edges of it, I could see about a thousand web pages, all flickering up and down, as if the computer was searching through them, reading them all. As the pictures went by, I could see they were all children's websites, and toys, and games, and all the sorts of things children do on the internet.

In the middle of the screen, something else was happening. Something that really made me think. In the middle of the screen, the computer was actually writing. Not printing things that someone else had written, but it was actually writing itself. I could see that, because words kept appearing and changing and switching around, as we watched. Words kept being pulled in from all the websites that were flying by.

I saw the word "pink" flash up, and then the word "fluffy". The computer was writing a Magic Fairies book all on its own!

"Quick!" I said to Adam. "Don't look at the screen!" I didn't want Adam to turn all funny like the other children. I told him what was going on.

I don't think he really got it (neither did I, really), but he said, "I'm going to smash the computer!" Smashing things is Adam's answer to most problems, and sometimes it helps, but I've noticed with computers that it usually doesn't.

"No," I said. I didn't try to explain that what you see on a computer isn't actually living there - it's actually living on the internet, so smashing the computer just stops you from seeing the thing. It doesn't stop it happening. Instead, I just said, "We have to be more clever." Adam stopped and looked at me. I knew he was waiting for me to be clever, and I knew that I had to hurry up because if I didn't say anything he'd go back to his idea of smashing, really quickly.

"We have to smash the printer!" I said. I knew it wasn't a great plan. The best plan was to find out what on Earth was going on, why the computer was writing the books, talk to the person who was making it happen, discover what to do about it and then do that.

In the end, though, I decided to go with Adam's plan. There were really three reasons for that, because just then:

1) I looked out through the door of the office and saw that the forklift robot was back. Not only that, but it had also brought lots of its forklift robot friends with it. They were heading towards the door of the office in a big, long line.

2) I noticed, in the corner of the office, there was a box. On the box, it said, "Magic Fairy doll prototypes" (a prototype is a test version of something that you make when you're planning to make lots more later). Inside the box, I could see a big pile of pink dolls with pink wings. The thing that made me notice them was that the doll on the top of the box had a horrid plastic face, with a strange smile painted on it, and I saw its eyes slowly open, and its head turn to face me. Underneath it, all the little pink wings of the other dolls started to flutter.

3) I looked at Adam, and it was pretty clear that the only thing Adam was thinking about was breaking the printer.

Sometimes, the best plan is not the best plan. Sometimes, the best plan is the only plan you can actually make happen right here, and right now. I knew we were going to need to run away and I also knew Adam was going to have to smash something, so that was the best I could do.

I pointed to the box of dolls, and Adam grabbed it. We ran through into the printing room, and Adam threw the box as hard as he could into the workings of the machine. Magic Fairy dolls flew out of the box and jammed themselves into the wheels, and the gears, and the robot arms.

Some of the Magic Fairy dolls got squashed by the giant rollers and flattened onto the pages of the Magic Fairy books. Some of them jammed into the gears of the machine, smashing into little plastic pieces in the machine. Some of them fell into the robot arms and were cut into pieces by the knives.

But I knew one thing about computer printers. They are very easy to break. We have four broken ones at home, and at school, there are about ten that are broken, almost all the time.

I could see that this one was broken now too. The printer was making some very strange noises, and one of the big reels of paper fell out, and bounced down onto the floor, rolling across in front of the row of robot forklifts, wrapping them in paper.

We only had a couple of seconds before they broke free, and I could see that two of the Magic Fairy dolls had escaped from the machine and were starting to follow us. One of them turned its head to look at me, and without changing its strange, grinning face, it said, "Stop running, little girl." Then it said, "Stop running, and buy more Magic Fairy books."

I thought it sounded creepy. I grabbed Adam, who was jumping up and down, laughing at all the chaos, and we ran for the door.

The robot arms all stopped packing books and started trying to grab us as we ran past and out into the big room, with all the piles of books. We got away from them, but we weren't in a much better place because that was when all the robot forklifts suddenly tore out from their roll of paper and started chasing us.

We were running down between the rows and rows of boxes towards the big doors, and up ahead, I could see them starting to close.

I shouted to Adam, and he dived towards the door, rolling over, and through the gap. I dived after him, and we both managed to scrape through. We dodged around the side of the factory, and I looked back in time to see a robot forklift stuck in the door. The door was starting to open again to let it out, and at the top of the door, two Magic Fairies flew out after us.

While they were getting through the doors, we had a little bit of time to run along the side of the building towards the street outside. I knew they would be after us, so we had to keep running, but then something really odd happened. We ran past a window in the factory, and I glanced inside. A man was sitting in an office. He was talking into the telephone, but as he saw me run past, he dropped the phone and stared out of the window after me.

It was only for a second, and I couldn't be sure, but suddenly a lot of things started making sense and I started to have a really bad feeling. I knew the face in the window. It was Mr. Johnny Chuckles!

I kept running, but also I kept thinking. I remembered Granny's party, and I remembered the way he had looked when we'd found him locked in the office after the magnet monster had been destroyed. I remembered what we'd locked him in there with. And I thought about the books, and the mysterious authors, and how we'd seen the computer writing the stories.

JC & PM. It couldn't be, could it? Really? Johnny Chuckles and... Present Machine?

My Present Machine? The code I wrote, to go out onto the internet, and look for things that boys and girls want - and the loop that my brother had put in, looping the list back into the learning part of the code. To take the things that boys and girls wanted, and feed them back to them, and then look again at what they'd wanted, and then feed that back. Over and over, again and again, learning all the time, growing all the time. And Johnny Chuckles - always looking at graphs of what he thinks everybody wants.

It was all beginning to make sense. If the Present Machine was now clever enough to write books, and it was on the internet, then it was easily clever enough to control robots as well. In fact, we probably had to guess that it could control pretty much anything electronic on the internet.

And that could be a big problem, because, if you think about it, almost everything is electronic and on the internet.

The forklifts were beginning to catch up with us as we ran as fast as we could out of the big factory gates, and into the street.

I thought I heard someone behind us shouting, "Wait, we need you! We need your granny!"

Of course he did. We were the ones who wrote the code. That was when I decided it would be best to go to the hospital and kidnap Granny.

You see - the beginning of the story all makes sense now, doesn't it?

Except what didn't make sense was - well - everything else. The flying fairies, the mad hypnotised children, the things that happened on the steam train (oh, no, that's right, we haven't got to that yet, have we?)

Part 3:

Act Normal And Don't Tell Anyone About

The Big Problem With Trains

Chapter 17

So, where are we up to? That's right - the hospital. You know, I really hadn't planned it this way, but we're about halfway through the story, and we're still exactly at the place we were at on page one! But quite a lot has happened already, and I hope you understand that you really had to read about it before this would all make sense.

Well, we ran into the hospital, and all the robot forklifts were too big for the doors so they had to stay outside. Granny's room was deep inside the building, but we found it quite easily. So far, so good, but I knew we couldn't stay in the hospital, because, out of the window, I could see more and more of the robots from the factory arriving.

They couldn't get in, but they could start surrounding the building, and that meant a siege. A siege is when you have an enemy outside a building, and you inside, and nobody can get in or out.

The problem with sieges is that they don't usually end well for the people inside, because eventually they run out of food and toilet paper. That's why I try to avoid being in sieges at all, if I can. I've only been in four or five of them ever.

We didn't have time to explain to Granny why we were kidnapping her, we just grabbed her wheelchair and ran. Granny was only just getting better from her fall, so she was a bit floppy and a bit tired, but she does like a good escape, so she woke up pretty quickly as we ran off down the corridor towards the back door.

Chapter 18

The doctors gave up chasing us just outside the main door, but the factory robots were after us by then, so we couldn't slow down. I knew we couldn't outrun them forever. Robots keep going until their batteries go flat, and Adam can pretty much run all day, but Granny's wheelchair wasn't really supposed to go as fast as it was, and the motor was starting to smell a bit burny - like a hairdryer when you leave it turned on in a box of Lego.

There was also the small problem of the Magic Fairies. The ones that Adam hadn't thrown into the workings of the printer were following us, and I could see them, like little dots in the sky above us.

As we zoomed through the streets, I thought quickly. If the Magic Fairies were alive, then that meant they weren't really Magic Fairies. Magic in real life is a bit rubbish - it doesn't really work, ever - whatever grown-ups say. In real life, everything people say is magic is really science, and you get on a lot better if you just treat it as science from the start.

That meant the Magic Fairy dolls were robots, and they were all really controlled by the Present Machine - just like the factory robots. And that meant there was another question - about why you would build a lot of robot toys and write books to make all the children buy them if you controlled them yourself - but that was a question for some time when I wasn't running. It began to feel as though there would never be a time when I wasn't running.

I decided we needed a faster way to escape. There was a train station just at the end of the road, so I shouted to Adam, and we skidded round and dived in through the door. The nice lady at the platform saw we had a wheelchair and opened the gate to let us through, without even asking to see our ticket.

"Hurry up!" she said, "We're about to leave!" Behind me, I heard a robot forklift smash into the station doors. I decided that it was probably too late to explain to the lady that we didn't have a ticket, and that we were being chased by robots controlled by a computer code I had written to search for presents, and that we had to escape before the toy robot Magic Fairies arrived.

She didn't look like the sort of person who heard that sort of thing very often, so I just said, "Thank you," and we came out onto the platform. That was when we saw it.

"Wow!" said Adam.

It was a real train.

There are two types of train. There are the ones you normally see, and you ride on, whenever you go anywhere. They're pointy, and quiet, and plasticky, and they get you where you're going really quickly. But they're a bit disappointing. The reason they're a bit disappointing is that the trains you see in pictures and in films and in toys, are always completely different.

Those trains are huge and metal, and great big clouds of smoke and steam come out at the top and at the sides. They're all covered in wheels and pistons and absolutely no plastic at all. They look like proper, real machines driven by people who get dirty driving them.

And this train - our train - was one of those. Adam was just standing staring at it. Neither of us had ever seen a "real" train before, and trains are Adam's third favourite things, after tanks and monsters.

"It's the Orient Express!" said Granny, "Are we going on the Orient Express?" Granny didn't have time to explain to us that the Orient Express was a very old steam train that used to go all through Europe and down into places like Istanbul, in Turkey. But nowadays it's usually just used for rich people to have birthdays and parties on, while it goes a little way around England.

Once I'd grabbed Adam and we'd scrambled up into the train and found a seat (which was not easy - the Orient Express is not well designed for getting on with a wheelchair when you're being chased), Granny did explain it to us, and Adam said he felt a bit sad that the train didn't go very far any more. I don't think Adam could have planned everything that happened after that just so he could take the Orient Express on one last trip across the world, but it might well have popped into his mind when he was thinking about how to solve The Big Problem With Trains.

Anyway, that's later on. Right then, we were sitting in some lovely, comfy leather chairs in a train that looked like a smoky smelly giant engine on the outside, and an old country house on the inside. I looked out of the window, and realised the train hadn't started moving yet, and inside the ticket office, I could see some of the robots starting to break through the barriers.

Suddenly, a man dived through the doors and onto the platform. He started to run along the side of the train, looking in through the windows. It was Mr. Johnny Chuckles, and he looked panicked.

Just as he got to our window, and saw us sitting there, the train, very slowly, started to move.

Mr. Johnny wasn't going to give up. He ran along the platform, trying desperately to keep up. He was waving his hands and shouting. Steam was coming from the train wheels, and the sound of the engine was a loud hissing, swooshing, thundering noise, so that all I could hear was bits of what he was shouting.

"We need you!" he shouted. "You've got to help me!" But then the train was going too fast for him, and the platform was running out, and the steam was blowing up, and he was lost in the cloud and the noise.

I wondered what he wanted. But I didn't wonder for very long, because as soon as we turned round, there was a man in a conductor's uniform standing right beside us.

"Can I see your tickets, please?" he said, in a voice that sounded like, "You really had better have tickets!"

Chapter 19

Granny just looked at the conductor, and smiled. In the kindest, sweetest voice, she said, "Tickets? Oh yes, tickets." She started patting her pockets pretending to look for tickets "I wonder if they're in our luggage," she said. "Is it right at the other end of the train? Do you want me to go and check?" She started to jerk her wheelchair back and forward, turning and crashing, back and forward, and around, as though she had never tried to control a wheelchair in her life (normally, she is great at controlling her chair - she had even escaped a load of doctors and robots, remember). She was blocking the whole train corridor, and nobody could get past. And all the time, she kept saying things like:

"Ooh…which way is forward?" And, "I get so confused, you know, about where I put my tickets!" In real life, I have never seen Granny ever get confused about anything, even differential calculus. "They all have such tiny writing on them, don't they? And I lost my glasses." She didn't say she lost them when she made them into an anti-magnet monster laser.

Then, when she was halfway round, she said, "These are my grandchildren you know, Adam and Jenny. They're lovely, but they're a bit of a handful. Would you mind looking after them while I look through all the luggage?"

The guard looked at me (I was trying to put the proper gears back into the wheelchair, so it didn't go so fast all the time) and then at Adam (Adam was standing on the table, doing a dance).

"Don't worry!" said the guard. "I'm sure they're all in order." He walked away. When I thought about it later, I decided it was very clever. Granny hadn't even had to tell a lie - not really.

"Now," said Granny to me, "do you mind telling me what we're doing on the Orient Express?"

I suppose it was a good question for her to ask, and I did my best to answer it with the bits that I understood. I told her that my code for the Present Machine had gone out of control, and was chasing us. That it had somehow gone from just learning what kinds of toys and books lots of boys and girls like, on the internet, to actually writing books, and using them to tell the children to buy toy dolls. I wasn't sure what the Magic Fairy dolls were going to do, once they got into shops and children started buying them, but it sounded like they would probably tell the children to buy more books.

Granny nodded. "It's dangerous," she said.

"Why?" said Adam.

"Remember, at my party, when Mr. Johnny Chuckles turned on his microphone, and whatever he wanted to say was made louder by the speakers, and then the microphone took it and made it even louder, and then it just kept getting louder and louder and louder?" I did remember. It was like a loop, with whatever sound came out just being fed back in and being made louder and more horrible all the time. "It's like that with people," she said. "If you only ever give boys a choice of tanks and monsters, and you only ever give girls a choice of fairies and unicorns, and then ask them what they want, then that's all they'll say, because that's all they can think of. Then it will just keep going round and round, with boys getting more boyey and girls getting more girly until everyone is sort of hypnotised into being more and more like everyone else."

I didn't like the sound of that. It sounded like a kind of trap. I told Granny about how we'd destroyed the printer.

"Well, that's a start," she said. Then I told her the Present Machine was making the robots chase us. "If it's on the internet, it can probably control anything electronic," said Granny. I'd wondered about that, and it didn't sound good.

"It's lucky we're on a steam train!" said Adam.

"I wonder why they want us," said Granny. I was about to answer, when I heard shouting from outside the window. I looked

103

out. There was a forklift robot driving along beside the train. It was bumping along, and only just keeping up. Mr. Johnny Chuckles was balancing on the roof, waving and shouting at us.

"We have to find…" he shouted, and then the forklift went over a bump, and he bounced off the roof, grabbing the back of the forklift as he fell. Now he was holding on with his fingertips, with his whole body flying out of the back of the forklift, flapping and waving like a flag. "You have to find your grandad!" he screamed. Then the forklift hit another bump, flipped through the air, and dug its forks into the ground, spinning Mr. Johnny up into the air, and throwing him in a big arc, and down into a patch of stinging nettles. As the train roared past, he sat up, still waving and shouting.

"Grandad?" said Granny, looking shocked. "How does the Present Machine even know anything about him?" But I didn't have time to wonder what it all meant, because that was when I saw the girls.

I guess it was supposed to be a party. A party for some very rich children whose parents could afford to have their parties on a steam train… and give away party bags containing brand new, not-even-in-the-shops-yet toys, like MAGIC FAIRY DOLLS!

Chapter 20

The girls were all sitting reading Magic Fairies books. There was the kind of absolute, total silence you never, ever get in a children's party. Nobody was arguing. Nobody was playing It. Nobody was speaking. None of the girls even looked up from their books at each other, or the steam train, or the countryside rushing by outside. The grown-ups didn't seem to have noticed. I think they were just pleased about the quiet. There was even a birthday cake sitting on the table, and nobody was staring at it. The candles had burned right down, and nobody had even blown them out. It was strange. Strange and creepy, and wrong.

But what caught my eye was one of the grown-ups coming back along the train. She was carrying an armful of party bags, and poking out of each bag was a Magic Fairy doll. They were all still in their wrappers, and they all had their eyes shut tight as though they were turned off, or sleeping. I could see their lacy pink dresses, and their painted-on smiles, all the same.

When the grown-up put the bags on the table, all the girls suddenly looked up. Without speaking, each girl reached out, and took a doll. I saw the girl nearest to me stare at her doll, and suddenly, she got the same smile as the doll had.

"Magic Fairy dolls!" said all the girls, all at the same time. The eyes on the doll held by the girl nearest me slowly opened, and

106

the doll and the girl stared at each other. The doll's eyes flashed. All the other girls were doing the same thing with their dolls. You know when you have a very special toy - one which is your most important toy in the world - it's sometimes like that toy is talking to you in your head? You and the toy can have whole conversations - whole adventures together just by looking at each other - as if you know what each other is thinking.

I mean, you know, it's not real, and everything, but it feels like that's what's going on. Well, you know that only ever happens with a very special toy, and hardly ever straight out of the box (you need to have a few games with a toy before you get that feeling). Well, it felt as though the dolls and the girls were talking to each other through their minds right away - the second they opened their flashing eyes.

Suddenly, all at once, the dolls' heads turned to face Granny, and Adam, and me.

"Come on!" I said. "We've got to run!" Then, all the girls' heads turned to look at us too, all at the same time. Granny saw what was happening, and got her wheelchair running down the middle of the train, with Adam and I running in front. Behind us, I could hear the girls tearing the wrappings off their Magic Fairy dolls, and climbing over the seats to run after us.

We ran to the end of the carriage, and threw open the door, bursting into the next carriage (which was a restaurant car with tables and chairs, and people drinking wine and eating crab pâté relaxing on a bed of Swiss chard). I slammed the door after Granny but the girls had nearly caught up with us. They were crowding in around the door as I pulled it shut. Each one was holding their doll, and smiling with the same strange grin.

We ran through the restaurant, and I knew the girls were following because I heard the whine of a wine glass flying past my ear, and a shard of chard hit me in the back of the head. I grabbed a crab and threw it backwards at them as we raced through to the next carriage.

The next carriage had a dance going on in it (I told you, this was a very posh train) and we dodged round a couple doing the cha-cha-cha, in between two people doing a quickstep, and almost over a row of old gentlemen doing the macarena right in front of the band at the end of the carriage (yes, there was a band in the train too). Granny skidded around the surprised-looking singer, and I ducked under the trumpet player. Adam wasn't so careful. He dived straight at the drummer, crashed into the cymbal, kicked the bass drum, flipped over the top of the whole drum kit and ran across all the little drums in a big circle, making a wild, crashing beat.

This was actually a really great idea by Adam, because the strange beat made all the dancers go crazy, trying to keep up, and everybody crashed into everybody else behind us, making a huge pile of dancing people that the girls, and their fairies, couldn't get past, and giving us just enough time to crash through into the coal store at the very front of the train, and lock the door.

The coal store was outside, and it was dirty. There was a huge skip full of coal on one side, and a small walkway, just wide enough for Granny's wheelchair, down one side, leading to the engine room. We could see all the girls and their dolls crushed up against the door, but none of them could get through. We were safe, for the moment, but I could see them starting to play with the lock.

"Look out!" shouted Adam. He had climbed up on top of the coal, I think he did that JUST to get dirty and covered in steam, but he was pointing out over the roof of the train, and when I looked up, I could see Mr. Johnny Chuckles, running along the top towards us, wobbling from side to side as the train bumped along the track.

"Stop! Stop!" he was shouting. "You've got to listen to me!" Then suddenly, everything went black. Black and very smoky. The train had gone into a tunnel - and not just any tunnel. This was the Channel Tunnel. The long, long tunnel that connects Britain to France!

After that, things got a bit confusing. I couldn't see very much, because of the dark, and the smoke, and because lots of things were happening at once.

Mr. Johnny was still shouting in the dark, but he sounded more frightened than angry, and he was definitely getting closer. At the same time, I could see the fairies on the other side of the door. They were putting their little robot hands inside the lock, and it was beginning to turn. On top of the train, Adam had found a sort of chain on a pulley with a grabby thing on the end of it. I think it was something the driver used to get the coal down to put in the engine, but Adam was unwinding it, and dragging it to the back of the train.

I looked down. The front of the train, where we were, was connected to the back by a sort of pin. I could see there were gears and a lever. I knew if I didn't do something, we would be caught pretty quickly, so I reached down and pulled the lever.

The gears spun round, and the pin connecting the two carriages popped up. Now the back of the train was loose, and while it started to slow down, the front, with us on, started to speed up, because it wasn't having to drag all the girls, and the restaurant, and the dancers. Slowly, we started to speed away from the back of the train, and the girls, and the fairies.

At that moment, out of the clouds of steam above the train, Mr. Johnny Chuckles appeared. Balancing on the top of the carriage, he jumped as hard as he could, across the gap, towards us. His fingers just caught onto the top of the coal truck, and he crashed into it, sliding to the floor in front of us.

"You've got to help me!" he cried. "I'm running away from the Present Machine!" He looked at Granny and me, and wailed, "I think I've done something really bad!"

I really wanted to know what, but it was a bad time to ask, because, just then, I looked up and saw Adam.

Adam doesn't think, or plan things the way I do, but sometimes, he can come up with brilliant ideas without thinking about them (although they usually cause chaos). My brother was swinging the grabby thing on the chain, and all he kept saying was, "I know how to fix The Big Problem With Trains!"

I didn't know what he was talking about, but he kept going on about "The Big Problem With Trains". My brother loves trains, and I didn't think there was a Big Problem With Trains, as far as he was concerned.

"Forget trains," Mr. Johnny shouted up at him, "we have to get to your grandad, and he's in India! And this train doesn't go to India!" Adam just kept swinging the big hook.

"That's The Big Problem With Trains!" he shouted back, and I started to understand. He threw the hook out of the back of the train, and smiled. I watched the hook fly through the air, but it missed the back half of the train and crashed into the ground between the rails. I looked at my brother. He was still grinning.

"Hold on!" said Granny in a voice that sounded like she really meant it. We all held on.

There was a jolt as the chain went tight, and the hook dug into the track. It was such a big jolt that it nearly stopped the train on its tracks, but instead, it pulled the track up behind the train into a curve. Then the back part of the train caught up, and crashed into the rail, pushing the bent track high into the air until it curved over the ceiling of the tunnel.

It made a screeching noise, and I could only just hear my brother shouting, "The Big Problem With Trains is that they can only ever go where the track goes!" The back carriages of the train pushed the torn-up piece of track right up over the whole engine, and it curled back down in front of the front wheels.

Once that happened there was another bump as the weight of the wheels on the track pressed the back part of the track down onto the front part.

Do you see what had happened? Do you see what my brother's plan was?

There was now a whole piece of bent track going under the train's wheels, then round to the back, then up and over the whole train and back down in front in a big loop. Adam had fixed The Big Problem With Trains, by giving the train a loop of track it could use forever, like a tank track. Now our train could go anywhere!

Chapter 21

Unfortunately "anywhere," still meant down the tunnel, and when we shot out of the tunnel at top speed, "anywhere" meant right through the middle of the town of Calais. Even worse, as we rushed down towards the front of the train, we saw the driver jump out. The moment he saw that we had changed the train into a rolling, go-anywhere train with its own portable rail, and that it was zooming down the middle of the main road through the city, he jumped out of the train and ran away.

Some people are like that when they see a little bit of chaos.

By now, most of the cars in the main street had got out of the way. I suppose that's what you do when you see a steam train coming towards you along the road. There were quite a lot of people shouting, and I started by trying to explain to them, politely, that things were a bit difficult for us at the moment and that none of us knew how to drive a steam engine.

I don't think many of them understood. Possibly because I don't speak French.

"I know how to drive a steam train," said Adam. My brother has certainly got a lot of books about steam trains, and he has definitely spent a lot of time playing at driving a steam train. He has even got several toy steam trains of his own, but I was not sure that meant that my brother actually did know how to drive a steam train.

The other problem was that this was not just an ordinary steam train. This was a steam train which had been changed so it could go anywhere, and probably nobody, even the actual driver of the steam train, knew how to drive one of those.

But then, also, Adam had been the designer and builder of this new type of steam train, and so, even though nobody in the world actually knew how to drive it, probably Adam was the person with the best head start.

He pulled levers, and whirled little wheels around, and looked at gauges. I don't think he understood the gauges, but he had seen other people looking at gauges on videos, so I think he knew you had to look at them. Most of the gauges were flickering with their needles pointed right over into the red section.

There were lots of screeches and hissing sounds. We got to the end of the road and, just as we were about to crash into a building, we suddenly swerved around a corner. The train seemed to be doing roughly what Adam wanted it to do.

"How did you do that?" I said to Adam. He said something about different brakes on different wheels, which sounded interesting, but then I looked behind us and realised that we were being chased by quite a lot of different people.

Chapter 22

Some of them were police. Some of them were angry car drivers. Some of them were robots which were crashing out of factories on either side of the road. It seemed like the Present Machine had got control of everything electronic in the world now. Luckily, we were in a steam train.

We zoomed on. I noticed that children were filling the streets, pouring out of every school playground. They weren't taking much notice of us, but they all had Magic Fairies and Tank Monsters books, and they were fighting - girls against boys - just like in our school.

It seemed to me that the whole world was going mad. But then, if everyone is doing something, apparently it's not mad any more, even if it is mad really. That's why I invented wierdNormal.

Up ahead, the police had set up a road block by parking their cars in front of the train. That was really silly of them for two reasons:

1) It was silly because we were in a TRAIN and a train is a lot heavier and less crumply than a car, and if you know anything about what happens when something very heavy and very strong hits something much lighter and more crumply, then you'll understand why the roadblock was silly.

2) The roadblock was only on the road. I pointed to the field beside the road, and Adam nodded. He whizzed a few wheels, and the train bumped off the road, and we zoomed off across the field, away from all the children and the police, and the people chasing us.

There is a lot of countryside in France, and, really, if you stay out of the way of towns, the countryside goes right the way down through Germany, Austria, Hungary and Romania.

It's actually quite peaceful, once you get the hang of it, even when the whole world is going mad. I looked down at Mr. Johnny Chuckles, who Adam and Granny had told to shovel coal into the steam engine's boiler. His clothes were all dirty, and he had soot all over his face and hands. He looked unhappy.

Now, it was time for some questions…

"What do you mean, you've made a mistake?" I said.

"I thought your code was just a way to find out what boys and girls like," he said.

"It was," I said, "but I think it learned too quickly - and now it's trying to tell people what they have to like."

"That's what the dolls are," he said. "The books tell people to buy the toys. Then the toys are going to tell them what to read. It just goes round and round and round!"

"Why did you help it?" I said.

"It tells you what you want," said Mr. Johnny. "It sort of hypnotises you. As soon as I realised what was happening, I ran away, but now it's after me too!" Mr. Johnny looked up at me. "We have to stop it."

"They're very clever," said Granny. "These Magic Fairy dolls."

Mr. Johnny shrugged. "We've got the best toy designer in the world," he said.

"But there are just a few dolls," I said.

"And I put most of them in the printer," said Adam. Mr Johnny looked even sadder.

"But there's a factory in India making thousands of them right now!" he said. "Very soon, everyone will have one! That's why we have to find your grandfather."

"What's he got to do with this?" said Granny. "I still don't see how the Present Machine even knows about him!"

I thought about it. Then I realised. Remember when we were in the office at Granny's party, and I wanted to be sure to remember everything Granny was saying about Grandad? Do you remember how I did it?

That's right. I added a recording block to my code for the Present Machine. That means that everything Granny said about Grandad, and what a great inventor of toys he was, had gone straight into the Present Machine's memory.

I got a horrible sinking sort of feeling.

"Is our grandad designing the Magic Fairy dolls?" I said. Mr. Johnny nodded. "Then we have to find him!" I said.

"I always hoped he would be somewhere doing good things," said Granny, sadly.

"He's in India," said Mr. Johnny Chuckles.

"Well then, young man," said Granny, "you'd better start shovelling coal."

Part 4:

Act Normal And Don't Tell Anyone About the Girls In The Factory

Chapter 23

It was a long time before we got to India. For days and nights, we kept our go-anywhere train going. We avoided the towns, because we didn't want anything electronic to see where we were going. I guessed that, by now, all the girls and boys in the world would probably be fighting each other.

It didn't seem possible, travelling through the countryside, past forests, and mountains, and through country after country, that in the towns and cities everyone was being so weirdNormal, but I knew it must be true. I also knew that really it was partly my fault. Granny said I couldn't have known what was going to happen when I coded the Present Machine, but I knew loops were dangerous. I also knew that when things got out of control, it happened fast, and it was always hard to know what was going to happen, so I still felt a little bit as if it was my fault.

I felt like the four of us, in our cross-country steam train, were the only people in the world who were being properly normal. And that was an odd feeling, because normally, I leave being normal to everyone else, because they're so much better at it than I am.

And halfway through Kazakhstan, I realised something else. The police from Calais had probably given up following us. The Present Machine probably had better things to do - like taking over the world and giving everyone in it what it had made them want. But, there was one person who would still be looking for us.

I felt suddenly so upset, I nearly cried. I went and stood by the back of the engine, and looked back over the countryside and into the distance.

It was Dad. I'd told Dad we were just going out to play. That was days ago, and here I was in a country I had never even heard of, on a stolen train, with a stolen Granny. I have never done anything that bad before. Even when I kidnapped the Prime Minister, I always made sure Dad knew which country we were in.

Eventually, we got to India. Mr. Johnny Chuckles knew where to take us to find Grandad, but we thought it was best to park a little way out of town. We thought it was possible that it might attract too much attention to turn up at his door in a giant steam train with its own tracks.

Adam skidded the train to a stop behind some trees just outside town, and we all climbed down from the engine and walked in on foot. Granny's wheelchair bumped along the rough road. She didn't say much, and she looked very tired.

It hadn't occurred to me before, but Granny wasn't in hospital for fun. She was there because she was not well. Taking her on a chase across the world, followed by an army of robots and fairies, to find the father of her child - someone she hadn't seen for years, and didn't really want to meet again - probably wasn't the best thing to make her better. I asked if she was OK. She just smiled, and pushed the button to zoom her wheelchair forward.

Soon, we reached a little house, standing on its own just outside town. I knocked on the door, and, after a long time, it opened. The man standing in the doorway was tall. He looked out at us without saying anything. His face looked as if it had forgotten how to smile a long, long time ago.

"Anton," said Granny, "do you remember me, from the big party in America?" Grandad just stood there not saying anything "These are your grandchildren." said Granny. "We're here to stop the fairies!"

Grandad still didn't say anything. He just stood, staring at us as if he didn't understand what was happening. "Well," said Granny after a while, "we're coming in whether you like it or not!" She pushed her wheelchair forward past him and into the house, and we all followed.

Chapter 24

"I don't think he can understand you," said Mr. Johnny, waving his hand in front of Grandad's face. He hadn't moved, or said anything, since we arrived. I've seen people do this before. It's the kind of look grownups sometimes get when they see something so strange that they get shocked into not knowing what to do.

It's like inside them there is one voice shouting, "Run away," and another voice is shouting, "Stay and do something," and their brains just can't decide which to do, because it's all so new to them, so they just stand and don't do anything - which is always the worst idea, because, usually, there are dinosaurs, or something. Kids don't do that, I've noticed, because literally EVERYTHING is new to us anyway, so we're used to it.

But I don't think it was that. I mean, all we were was an old lady, two kids and a party organiser. We shouldn't have been that surprising to Grandad. We didn't even have our steam train with us. I bet he's seen lots more surprising things than that.

It wasn't until a long time after, when I thought about it again, that I thought we weren't just two kids. He had spent his whole life living alone, and we were two grandchildren he never knew he had. That was probably a pretty surprising thing for him.

But even then, I don't think it was that, because I have seen that look in other places too. I saw it on Mr. Johnny Chuckles, when we let him out of the office, that first time he saw the Present Machine, and I saw it on the faces of the girls on the train with the dolls, and the children in our school playground fighting over whether Magic Fairies or Tank Monsters were best.

"It's the Present Machine," said Mr. Johnny, "it sort of hypnotises you. It finds out what you want to hear, and then it keeps repeating it back to you over and over again."

"That doesn't sound like it would hypnotise you," I said.

"Pretty soon," said Mr. Johnny, "it starts telling you what you want, as well as asking you what you want. And in the end, you can't tell the difference between what you want and what it wants you to want."

But I wasn't listening any more. I was looking at something Adam was playing with in the corner of the room. It was a big pile of papers. I grabbed them, and started reading through as fast as I could.

The papers were all instructions. There were the designs for the Magic Fairy dolls, which the Present Machine had made Grandad design for it. But there were also papers about a factory, where the dolls were being made. There were tables showing how many dolls were being made, and when they were being sent out to the toy shops all around the world.

I looked at the numbers, and they were huge. This factory was making hundreds of thousands of Magic Fairy dolls - enough to make children all over the world just like the ones on the train. We couldn't let them be sent out, but the really big problem was the date on the bottom of the page.

All the dolls were being sent off TODAY, so that they would all be in the shops in time for Christmas. That meant that today was the only day we had to stop them! I threw the papers onto the floor, and told Granny we had to go to the factory right now.

Granny told Mr. Johnny to try to get Grandad to stop being hypnotised, and to look after Adam, while we were gone, and we zoomed on her wheelchair out of the house.

I should really have read all the papers. If I had read them all, I might have seen that the Magic Fairy dolls were not the only things being made at the factory, and we might have been ready for what happened when we got there. As it was, I didn't and we weren't.

Chapter 25

The toy factory looked, from the outside, just like any other factory, but as we crept secretly through the door at the back (you remember that I'd worked out about factories that the best doors for creeping were at the back), I suddenly saw something that made me stop and stare.

You know I said before that, sometimes, grown-ups brains just freeze, when they see strange things, and they don't know what to do? And you know I said that didn't happen to kids, because everything is new to us anyway? Well, I was wrong. Some things we do think we know, and when those things get messed with, even my brain freezes.

If you have never been to a factory somewhere like India, don't go. It will make you scared, and angry, and it will make you never want to use anything made in a factory ever again.

The factory was huge, and filled with giant machines and long tracks and conveyor belts. There were boxes, and tables piled high with bits of toys, ready to be put together. There were thousands of Magic Fairy wings, all piled up. There were Magic Fairy legs and arms, rolling along the conveyor belts, in long, long lines. There were racks of Magic Fairy doll heads, staring out with their strange smiles across the factory.

There were also other toy parts. Parts which I couldn't tell why they were there. Why does a Magic Fairy need a scaly tail, for example? Or a big gun? Where, on a Magic Fairy, would you find a big set of needle-sharp teeth?

But I wasn't taking much notice of any of that. What I was watching was the people - rows and rows of people - standing at the machines, and conveyor belts, putting the Magic Fairies together, one leg, and one arm, at a time. Popping on their tiny wings, and their little pink tutus. Clipping in the electronics in their brains that connected them to the Present Machine. I thought for a moment that all the machines were just extra big, so everyone looked small, but, as I watched, I realised that wasn't it at all. And that was what made my brain freeze.

They were children. All of the people working in the factory were children, just like me. I stood and stared. Hundreds of little girls were all working, just like grown-ups, all day making toys they would never get to play with for other children, like me, in other, richer countries.

I looked at Granny. She looked back at me.

"We have to be careful not to get caught," said Granny. She wheeled her chair back into the shadows behind a pile of boxes. But I wasn't listening. I was too angry. The place was silent. Absolutely quiet, apart from the sound of the machines. I didn't think it was possible for that many children to be that quiet. It was like sitting in school assembly, with an ear infection. It certainly wasn't right.

I marched over to the nearest conveyor belt, and stood next to the girl working there. She was about the same age as me. She should have been in school.

"Why are you working here?" I said.

"We're not supposed to talk," said the girl. She pushed a Magic Fairy arm into my hand, and showed me how to clip it into the bodies that were floating along the conveyor belt. I looked up, and saw there were cameras everywhere. I would have to Act Normal if I wanted to stay hidden, and Acting Normal here apparently meant putting Magic Fairy dolls together. I put a few arms in place on a few dolls, and watched them float off towards the next girl, who was clipping on legs. At least they didn't look hypnotised, I thought. I wondered how it was that all the other children in the world, and Mr. Johnny, and Grandad, had been hypnotised by the Present Machine, but not these girls.

"How long do we have to do this?" I whispered.

"All day," she said. "All day, every day."

I gasped. "When do you go to school?" And she just looked at me, sadly. I looked across at the girl on the other side of the conveyor, and at the ones to the left and the right. Then I looked out across the factory at all the hundreds of girls. No school. No school ever, for any of them.

"Why aren't you hypnotised?" I said, and she told me. The Present Machine had tried, but it couldn't do it, because the Present Machine couldn't tell them what they wanted, because it couldn't give them what they wanted. Because all the girls in the

135

factory only wanted one thing, and it was something that I already had, but I couldn't give to them either.

They wanted a school.

All any of the girls in the factory wanted was to go to school. But they couldn't go to school because their families were poor, and so they had to work in the factory instead.

This made me even more angry. It's making you angry too, isn't it?

Right at the far end of the factory was a huge screen. On it, pictures of the parts of the Magic Fairy dolls flashed up with instructions, one after another, repeating over and over again. At the sides of the screen were huge speakers. The biggest I had ever seen. They stretched from the floor to the ceiling, high above our heads. I couldn't imagine why you would need such huge speakers, but I think you probably can imagine. And I think, if you can imagine, you're probably getting even more worried about what will happen next. Anyway, I didn't think about that, and I didn't think about the huge tanks of dark, black liquid stored under the screen either.

What I thought about was the screen, and the set of metal steps leading up to the side of it. Because, right at the top of the steps, and connected to the screen, was a little keyboard, and a little computer mouse. I was starting to have a sort of idea.

That keyboard had to be connected directly to the Present Machine. If I could get up there, I could change the code. I started to think about how I might change my code to make the Present Machine a little bit less evil, and a bit less take-over-the-world-y.

It was a difficult problem, but there was an even more difficult one. There were cameras all over the factory, watching the girls. I couldn't see any guards, right now, but I was pretty sure there there must be some. The reason was this:

At school, my teacher, Mrs. Brisket, is very strict. We are very quiet when she is there. But if Mrs. Brisket goes out of the room for even one minute, we do not stay quiet. Even though we know she could be back at any second, and anyone who is noisy when she does will be in big trouble, there is still instant chaos. It's like adults have a sort of bubble with them. So long as we're inside the adult bubble, children can be quiet. But the moment a group of children goes outside the adult bubble, there absolutely has to be noise.

Now, I couldn't see any adults in the factory, but somehow, somewhere, I knew there must be someone or something in charge, because we were absolutely, definitely still inside the bubble. Children, in real life, are just not that quiet when nobody's watching them.

I looked back into the shadows to where I could just see Granny hiding, and I signalled to her that I was going to try to get up to the keyboard. Granny waved her hands in front of her, and shook her head really fast, which I thought probably meant, "Yes, that's a really good idea, go and do that!"

Then I swapped places with the girl next to me, very quickly, and started putting arms onto the dolls instead of legs. I did that for a bit, then I swapped places with the girl next to her, and took over clipping the bodies together. Each time I swapped, I was moving back along the line of girls, and closer and closer to the steps leading up to the keyboard.

And each time I swapped with a girl, I had a little, whispered conversation with her. "What do you want?" I said.

"I want a school," she always replied. And pretty soon, I started saying something back.

I said, "I will get you a school, if you help me."

I really meant it, but I knew it gave me another problem, and I didn't really need another problem. Now I had to somehow get the girls a school, as well as defeating the Present Machine, and all its little Magic Fairies, and getting everyone else in the world un-hypnotised before everyone got Magic Fairy dolls for Christmas and the world ended. It was all beginning to look a bit tricky.

I kept swapping places, getting closer and closer to the steps, and each time I did, I learned a new bit about how the Magic Fairy dolls got put together. I learned that putting the wings on was really fiddly, because they were really thin, and if you twisted them, they would fall straight off. I also learned that, on the other side of the factory, another line of girls was putting together something that wasn't Magic Fairies. Something with scaly tails, and needle-sharp teeth. Whatever it was ended up packed in boxes next to the boxes of fairies. Exactly the same kind of boxes that Granny was hiding behind.

By now, I was close to the bottom of the steps. I could see the huge speakers, and the big tank of black liquid, but I was still ignoring them, and thinking about how I could change the code on the Present Machine before I got caught by whoever was going to catch me.

I thought about the code. I wouldn't have time to change it all but, maybe if I changed a couple of blocks, I could do something. The Present Machine wasn't really evil, after all. It just wanted to give people what they wanted.

I looked up. At the other end of the factory, the big doors were starting to open. Outside, trucks were waiting to take all the toys out across the world in time for the quietest, most hypnotised Christmas ever. If I was going to do something, it had to be absolutely right now.

I still didn't have my whole plan, but I would have to think of the code when I got to the top of the stairs. I looked round. There didn't seem to be any guards, so I signalled to Granny. Just as I'd hoped, she started to cause a distraction. She zoomed her wheelchair out into the middle of the factory, and spun it around. Lights started to flash, and the huge speakers made a whooping alarm noise.

I took the chance, and ran for the steep metal stairs up to the keyboard. I got about halfway up before the sound of the alarm suddenly changed, and I knew I was in trouble...

Chapter 26

The sound changed, from a whooping alarm sound to a much, much lower noise, not at all like an alarm. It was a low, rumbling, farting sound. I think you know what that means. Except it wasn't like the farting sound we heard from the computer speakers in the office at Granny's party. It wasn't even like the loud farting sound that came from Mr. Johnny's speakers.

This was so loud that it tickled the insides of my ears and made my hair dance on its own, and so low that the metal stairs shook and rattled. I was just a couple of steps away from the keyboard, but, as I turned and looked down into the tank of black liquid under the screen, I knew I wasn't going to get to the top.

The liquid spiked suddenly, and I realised what it was. A huge liquid magnet monster. The sound changed and the monster rose up out of the tank, until it was as high as the ceiling. Huge tentacles shot out of its sides, and started to curl around, while the back of the monster rippled with spikes, like a hedgehog - if a hedgehog was made of liquid, and moving, and changing all the time.

It climbed and flopped out of the tank, and I could see it stretching out towards Granny's wheelchair. She dodged to avoid it, and the tentacle splashed-smashed into the floor. I made a dive for the keyboard, but suddenly a tentacle came out of nowhere. I felt a wet, warm splash around my waist, as though I had been grabbed by a dirty swimming pool, and I suddenly felt myself flying through the air.

I crash-landed into a pile of Magic Fairy boxes, right next to Granny, and the boxes toppled to the floor. I scrambled to my feet and grabbed Granny, pulling her away from the spiky tentacles, and we backed away from the monster, and towards the back wall of the factory.

All the girls from the factory were just standing, staring up as if they had never seen a giant magnetic liquid monster before. (Which possibly they hadn't. Even I had never seen one this big, and I thought I had seen all of them.)

We were trapped, but it was worse than that. When I knocked the boxes over, they had all split open, and covered the floor with thousands of Magic Fairy dolls. The dolls only took a moment to start opening their eyes, and turning their strange smiles towards us. Suddenly, the air was full of fluttering pink wings, and the Magic Fairy dolls were swarming towards us, through the air.

I remembered what I'd learned when I was making the fairies, and I grabbed the first few out of the air, and twisted - just like I had done on the conveyor belt. Their wings fell off, and the fairies dropped onto the floor, but there were many, many more, and they kept coming towards us. I knew there were far too many to catch.

I looked around. Behind the fairies, the monster stood up really tall, and stretched itself out like a wall, so that it blocked the way out while the Magic Fairies slowly closed in around us.

And that was when Adam crashed in through the wall, driving the strangest steam train I had ever seen in my life. It was made out of the second-strangest steam train I had ever seen in my life (and, I suppose, the only steam train I had ever seen in my life) - our steam train.

I could see Mr. Johnny shovelling coal into its boiler, and standing on the top of the roof, grasping a set of controls, was Grandad. I could see, in one second, that Grandad was not hypnotised any more. Somehow, Mr. Johnny and Adam must have got through to him, because this was the Grandad I had imagined, when Granny had told her story, back at her birthday party.

The mad, strange toymaker grandad, with the most impossible inventions.

The control he was holding was like a big mechanical arm, attached to some gears that looked as though they'd come out of the train engine. Big streams of steam shot out from behind Grandad every time he moved the arm, and from behind him, another huge arm reached up over his head, copying his movements. On the end of that arm was a giant, and I really do mean giant, bubble-making net. Grandad smiled and waved at us, as Adam skidded the train round in a big circle between us and the swarm of fairies. The giant arm waved too, and streams of bubbles rose out of it.

Then Grandad swept his arm round in a big circle, bringing the huge arm around and scooping hundreds of flying fairies into his huge net. He swooped his net around, and back again across the swarm, catching hundreds more, and throwing millions of bubbles into the path of the rest of the Magic Fairies. Grandad waved his hands, and the net flew back and forth through the air, until the net bulged with pink fairies, squished against the netting. Each time a bubble hit a fairy, it burst, soaking the fairy with soapy water, and gunging its wings together, so that it fell to the ground.

That was when I turned back to see Granny, and I realised things were going to get worse. Behind Granny, another pile of boxes

145

was starting to bulge and tear. Suddenly, it split right open, and from inside, can you guess what poured out?

No. Not more fairies. Something else.

Now I saw what the other girls had been making with the tails and the teeth. I should have known it. The Magic Fairy books were telling all the girls to buy Magic Fairy dolls. It hadn't occurred to me to wonder what the boys' books were telling them to buy!

Tank Monsters. Hundreds and hundreds of tiny Tank Monsters tore their way out of the boxes, and rolled and crawled towards us. One dropped into Granny's lap, and she grabbed it and threw it away, but at least a thousand more were coming.

I yelled to Adam, and he jolted the train forwards, speeding it around in a big circle, crushing little Tank Monsters under its rails, as they climbed up the wheels and started to bite and chew through the train's engine. Adam skidded the train around to flatten more of the monsters, but, of course, by moving the train, he'd stopped it from blocking the giant magnet monster!

I heard the farting sound change again, and the monster pulled itself up and over, ready to splodge down on top of us, in a giant tidal wave.

Suddenly, one of the girls from the factory screamed. I saw a ripple go through the side of the monster. It was just the tiniest little splash in the huge monster, but it gave me an idea. I actually had three ideas all at once.

The first was sound. Sound controlled the monster. Sound and magnets.

"Make a noise!" I shouted to the girls. "Scream! Shout! As loud as you can!" I was a bit afraid that these girls wouldn't know how to make a noise, after so long having to be quiet, but, as it turned out, they were just as good at it as the children in my school playground. The whole factory exploded into sound. The screaming, shouting children were so loud, they almost drowned out the monster's giant speakers.

The magnet monster started to ripple all over. Its tentacles reached out, but the screams and shouts of the children made it wave and wobble all over the place. But it wasn't beaten yet, and it started to crash and flop its way towards us. The screams weren't going to be enough to stop it, but that was my second idea.

I leapt at the conveyor belt. Next to it, there was a big red switch. I pulled it, and the conveyor started running in reverse, back into the factory. I knew the conveyor was powered by electric motors, and electric motors were magnets. With the conveyor going the wrong way, the monster started being pulled slowly back towards its tank.

It was still being driven forward by the speakers, and I knew that the moment the screaming and shouting stopped, it would be back. I could also see the Tank Monsters chewing their way through the Orient Express' engines, and Adam having to fight harder and harder to keep control. I could also see Grandad having to fight harder and harder to keep control of the net. The squished fairies were fighting back, tearing and pulling at the net. Holes were starting to appear, and fairies were squeezing through.

But that was my third idea. I leapt onto the conveyor, and ran along it. I was running in the same direction as it was now, so I was twice as fast as I normally am. I shot under one of the monster's tentacles as it splashed down behind me, and I jumped off onto the stairs up to the keyboard.

The monster turned. The Present Machine had seen where I was going, and I knew I would only have one chance. I would have time to change just one block in my code, but it didn't matter. I only needed to change one block.

I grabbed the top step, and pulled myself up, poking at the keyboard with my fingers. The code of the Present Machine sprang up on the screen. The sound in the room was deafening.

The farting sound of the monster wobbled the floor, throwing floor tiles up into the air, and shook the ceiling, so that the lights swung back and forwards. The grinding and hissing of the train, as the Tank Monsters tore it apart, filled the air, and the sound of the shouting girls hurt my ears. I could see, out of the corner of my eye, a tentacle spiking towards me as I clicked on the coding block I wanted, and switched it over.

Instantly, the sound from the speakers cut out. The tentacle splashed down into the tank, and the whole monster dissolved into black, sticky rain, covering everyone. The train skidded to a halt, and the Magic Fairies and Tank Monsters, with nothing now controlling them, froze.

Chapter 27

"What did you do?" said Mr. Johnny Chuckles, as he stepped down from the wrecked, half-eaten train. Adam was busy picking up the pieces of the Tank Monsters and the Magic Fairies. I think he was wondering if he could make a giant Tank Monster out of all of them, but I knew he'd need my help for that, and I wasn't going to help him.

"The Present Machine had a 'LEARN' block in it," I said. "I just swapped it for a 'TEACH' block. So now it's just waiting for somebody to tell it what to teach." Mr. Johnny Chuckles looked up at the giant screen. I said, "All these children need a school. Somebody should change this factory into a school."

"I've done something really bad, haven't I?" Mr. Johnny said. sadly, "I wish I could do something to make up for it, but I don't think I'm very good at parties." I felt a bit sorry for him.

"You're very good at getting people to do things," I said, "and you are good at fun when the fun has rules." Mr. Johnny shrugged, but he still wasn't getting it, so I said, "I think you'd make a good headmaster."

Finally, he got it. He looked up at the factory, and then at all the children wandering among the broken machines wondering what to do next.

"Come on, girls!" he said suddenly, "We've got a lot of work to do!"

I turned to Granny. Grandad was crouched down beside her wheelchair. I could see they were both crying. Remember how Granny had said that she left him at the big party, and she didn't go to find him when she knew she was having Dad because she thought he didn't want children? Well, it turns out, she was wrong about that.

"How did it get you?" said Granny. "What did you want?"

Grandad looked at her. He looked so sad. He spoke almost in a whisper. "Children," he said, eventually. "I wanted children. It's all I ever wanted."

Now, it was Granny's turn to look sad. "I should have told you," she said.

"It doesn't matter now," said Grandad, and he put his arm round her.

Suddenly, the back door of the factory flew open, and a car drove in. It skidded to a stop, and the door flew open. Dad got out.

"Well," he said, looking at me and Adam, "you've made quite a mess this time, haven't you?"

"How did you find us?" I said. Dad smiled.

"Do you think I couldn't find my children?" said Dad. "You leave a trail." I thought he meant footprints or something. But he didn't. "Chaos," he said. "You and Adam leave a certain kind of chaos wherever you go. It's as easy to follow, for me, as a satnav."

"I'm sorry," I said. Dad just hugged us.

"I wouldn't have it any other way," he said, and we all got into the car, ready for the long journey home.

"I expect you are going to punish me," I said to him while we were driving along.

Dad did punish me in the end, but not for destroying the factory, or for taking the train across the world. He didn't punish me for inventing the Present Machine, because he said he knew I wasn't trying to do anything wrong. And he didn't even punish me for nearly hypnotising all the children in the world - which was a pretty bad thing to have nearly happened.

But Dad did say I had got on the bus without asking him, and that was wrong.

For that, he banned me from doing experiments for a whole week, and I had to watch television instead, which was boring.

But it did give me time to think of lots of experiments I wanted to do later, including one very big one about time travel - but I'll tell you about that in another story.

Mr. Johnny Chuckles (now calling himself Mr. Chuck) rounded up some of the Magic Fairies, and sent them out to collect up all the Magic Fairy and Tank Monster books left in the world.

Without the books, the children could all get back to normal. I also emailed him, in India, to tell him to put a few more blocks into the Present Machine - just to let it look on the internet and see all the hundreds and thousands of mad, strange things that people liked. That confused it for a while, but in the end I think it worked out that there is no normal thing that everybody likes - and trying to guess at that sort of thing just makes everyone sad, because nobody is really normal, and everybody's normal is different.

Chapter 28

By the time we got Granny back to the hospital, she was not very well. The doctors told me I was wrong to take her on an adventure. They said she was in hospital because she was ill. They said she didn't want an adventure. She wanted rest. I thought about that a lot, because we spent a lot of time in the hospital over the next few weeks - me, and Dad, and Grandad, and Adam. Granny was given lots of drugs and hooked up to lots of machines, and she hardly woke up at all, and Grandad and Dad talked a lot about what had happened in all the years they hadn't known each other.

I don't know what's going to happen now, with Granny. She is very ill. Once, when we were all sitting round her bed, her eyes were closed and she wasn't moving. She started to make this noise, which sounded a bit like a wheezy sort of cough. Her whole body started shaking, and all the nurses rushed around her, until she calmed down again.

They all thought she was having a coughing fit, but I don't think so. I could see her face, and the corners of her mouth turned up. I think she was lying there, thinking about us, and about the monsters, and the train chases, and Grandad's bubble net full of Magic Fairies, and our great big adventure, all across the world. And I think Granny was laughing.

The End.

ACT NORMAL
AND DON'T TELL ANYONE ABOUT THE
ZOMBIE ROBOTS

Christian Darkin

ACT NORMAL
AND MAKE EVERYTHING
FAIR

Christian Darkin

ACT NORMAL
AND DON'T TELL ANYONE ABOUT THE
RHINOCEROS MAGNET

Christian Darkin

ACT NORMAL
AND DON'T TELL ANYONE ABOUT THE
LADDER INTO SPACE

Christian Darkin

ACT NORMAL
AND DON'T TELL ANYONE ABOUT THE
CASTLE MADE OF SWEETS

Christian Darkin

ACT NORMAL
AND DON'T TELL ANYONE ABOUT THE
DINOSAUR IN THE GARDEN

Christian Darkin

ACT NORMAL
AND DON'T TELL ANYONE THAT
CHRISTMAS IS EARLY

Christian Darkin

Things to do if you enjoyed this book:

1) Read some of the other books in the Act Normal series. Just type Act Normal into Amazon.

2) Get a FREE signed copy of one of the other Act Normal books, and practice your writing skills at the same time just by writing a review of this book! See **www.christiandarkin.wordpress.com/writing-now/** for details.

3) Ask your teachers to email me so that I can come to visit your school.

4) Get your parents or guardians to *like* **www.facebook.com/ActNormalBooks/** on Facebook. It's the best place to hear when new books come out.

5) And of course tell your friends to Act Normal and read more…

PLANT ACADEMY
THE COOKBOOK

PLANT ACADEMY
THE COOKBOOK

PLANT-BASED TECHNIQUES &
RECIPES FOR CREATIVE COOKING

LAUREN LOVATT

Photography by
Sara Kiyo Popowa
@shisodelicious

Leaping Hare Press

CONTENTS

STOCKS & SAUCES

NUTS & SEEDS

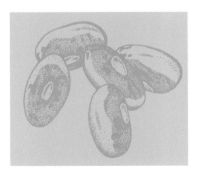

BEANS & LEGUMES

GRAINS & PSEUDO GRAINS

PLANTS
78

THE WORLD OF FERMENTATION
94

THE CHEESE MODULE
110

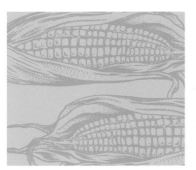

THE MISSING INGREDIENT
120

UNDERSTANDING ADAPTOGENS
134

GLUTEN-FREE BAKING
146

RAW DESSERTS
156

PLATING 101
168

FOREWORD

BY RICHARD BUCKLEY

Award-winning vegetarian chef & owner of OAK Restaurant, Bath

No recipe can make you cook well. In fact, if you dig deep enough, recipes aren't really a thing. A cookbook recipe is just a compendium of individual techniques brought together for the convenience of the novice. Talk to any serious cook or chef and you will find they think in terms of technique and base recipes and adapt them to the ingredients in front of them. It is like learning the sounds of a poem in a foreign language rather than the language itself; the former will allow you to recite the poem, the latter will allow you to understand and write endlessly yourself.

Every cuisine has its base recipes and techniques. Indians must learn the art of spice blending and the correct treatment of onions, the French have Escoffier and the Italians must master pasta. One of the problems with plant-based cookery is that it is, perhaps, the first post-modern cuisine to have emerged in a globalized world, united not by a place and people but instead by ideals and ethics. There are, however, thanks to the power of the internet and social media, common techniques, base recipes and ideas that most plant-based chefs draw upon.

These are often very different to those used by meat-based cooks and chefs and it is one of the major reasons why meat-based chefs often cook plant-based food so poorly. They simply don't have the vocabulary required.

It is a problem Lauren and I often discussed; there was nowhere a serious plant-based chef could go to learn the core techniques and become grounded in the basics. Whilst I often complained and dreamt of ways to address this problem, Lauren got up and did something. Founding the Plant Academy and subsequently the seminal courses Plant 1, 2 and 3, Lauren set about bringing together all of the top talent in the plant-based world to share not just their recipes and ethos but also their techniques.

This book is sorely needed and there is no-one better placed to write it. Lauren's cooking is beautiful and she has a profound understanding of the vocabulary of plant cookery. If you are serious about cooking with plants, then you need to learn and memorize every page of this book. I hope it becomes the culinary bible it deserves to be.

INTRODUCTION

WELCOME TO *PLANT ACADEMY: THE COOKBOOK*

This is the ultimate handbook for plant-based food, to teach you the building blocks of proper plant-based cooking. Here to make plant based-food practical and offering all the tools, information and inspiration you will ever need to cook well with plants.

WHAT IS PLANT-BASED?

So we are all on the same page before we dive in, 'plant-based' means eating food that comes from plants and contains no animal products. It differs to strict veganism, as eating plant-based indicates some flexibility – for example with using honey – and is more flexible in general lifestyle. Veganism means eating and living in a way where no animals are harmed in any way, including not wearing leather, and 'raw' means only eating foods that have not been cooked over 42°C. Vegetarianism is something entirely different, and involves eating animal-derived products including dairy and eggs, which we are not including in any way in this book.

WHY ARE WE HERE?

As a plant-based chef, culinary teacher and a vegan for 10 years, I have witnessed so many the plant-food trends. I have been asked the most wild and wonderful questions and immersed myself in many cultures to learn about good plant-based cooking. While teaching or talking to so many different people from around the world, I have noticed that although we have many great plant-based recipe books we don't yet have somewhere where techniques are provided to help us understand how to make satiating dishes with vegetables as the star.

We're still faced with the same old preconceptions that plant-based food takes too long to make, isn't filling or is missing something. So, with this book, I'm stripping things back to basics and teaching you techniques and ideas that can transform your kitchen into a treasure trove of natural foods.

In professional kitchens, I've found chefs have no problem adding creative flair to dishes and making the perfect quenelle, but when it comes from knowing the difference between a nut cream and butter they can appear lost. The same goes for home cooking: many of us are happy with the basics but aren't sure how to sizzle up a fully plant-based dinner without the centre of the plate coming from an animal or from an animal replacement.

With traditional cooking we may have perfected our soufflés, stocks and sushi, but when it comes to plant-based cooking the approach is not so straightforward.

There's a huge amount of information out there that can be more confusing than useful, so Plant Academy is here to put plant-based techniques in one place and keep it simple.

In this book I've combined fundamental base techniques with recipes that use them. I'm not trying to push any boundaries or reinvent your favourite animal meat, just encourage you to use whole ingredients and I hope the plant-based ideas will become part of your own repertoire and stay with you for life, in a way that genuinely makes an impact.

A BRIEF HISTORY OF PLANT-BASED EATING

Within the last decade in the West we've seen raw food, veganism and plant-based living each have their five minutes of fame. In the UK, following the 'wellness' boom when Deliciously Ella became a household name and an array of health-focussed institutions like Wild Food Café and Tanya's restaurant in London emerged, we are living at a time where junk food rules and a lot of what might be called 'plant-based foods' are in fact traditional dishes with substituted ingredients that aren't full of plants at all.

This is not a complete origin story of plant-based food but a recent story of modern plant-based eating in the UK. Plant-based foods are found in every culture around the world, and many, such as Indonesian gado gado, Mexican tacos de Jamaica (hibiscus tacos) and Japanese shojin ryori, are naturally plant-based. Many communities, such as the Jains in India, have long embraced plant-based eating. Our food landscapes and the diet of all human civilisations have historically been shaped by what grew and lived around us: for the vast

majority of cultures, seasonal plants, grains, seeds, animal products and fish have formed the base of our diets for all time. As time has passed, what started with simple processing of ingredients has become more and more complex and now processed food around the world has become sought after, whether for its convenience, status, price or taste. In the West in particular, the development of the processed and ultra-processed food industry and its commercialization led us to label our preferences and lose our connection with local, seasonal foods. We have, in general, fallen out of love with real ingredients and cooking, to the point that eating whole foods and cooking simply now seems radical and new. With a whole world of information at our fingertips, why are we still getting in a pickle about cooking with plants?

In England, known partly for its food culture of roast dinners and fish and chips, the hippies of the 60s started to eat alternatively partly as a form of activism. The first vegan society in England was established in 1970, and soon after, niche vegan books started emerging and vegan restaurants such as Mildreds in London began to flourish, although all welcoming a marginal audience rather than the mainstream. The first plant-based cookery school, Demuths, was established by Rachel Demuth in Bath in 2001, and Made in Hackney was London's first 100% plant-based community cookery school, opening in 2012. Prevalent chefs like Richard Buckley and Alexis Gautier, raw food pioneers like Kate Magic of Raw Living, and chocolate and dessert maker Amy Levin paved the way to the vegan boom in 2013.

You will learn more about the rich history of these ingredients and people who have paved the way for vegan food in the UK within each chapter, but to go deeper into this history of plant-based eating I recommend reading *No Meat Required* by American food and culture writer Alicia Kennedy. She dives into the history, politics and environment of plant-based eating, championing the trailblazers who helped us to get to where we are today, 'using activism through hedonism and pushing the boundaries with amazing cooking' and certifying this plant food thing is more than a trend but a rich lifestyle that can drastically impact and improve our future.

'That future is possible as has been imaged by the hippies in the farm, by Frances Moore Lappe, by punks and anarchists, by vegetarians and vegans, by fighters for food justice. The narrative is up for the taking. The history, the philosophy and the cuisine are written down for us to learn from to form a new world with, an abundant one, a caring one, a delicious one... I'm going to hope for better, for more, for everyone.'

Alicia Kennedy, No Meat Required

THE ORIGINAL PLANT ACADEMY

I opened Plant Academy culinary school in 2019, with the ambition to bring a different kind of food education to London. I had spent the first part of my food career involved in opening a vegan and gluten-free restaurant in the Cotswolds called Asparagasm, and saw people start to understand the concept of raw cakes and funky plant-based plates over the three years I spent there. I craved connections

with others who were as involved in this world as I was: after taking every short course I could find in England (there were few as none of the culinary institutions has yet grasped plant-based cuisine), I headed to LA to study at Matthew Kenney culinary, the place pioneering the plant-based food scene at the time.

Soon after training, I was offered a job at the culinary school and ended up opening an Academy for them in Barcelona. Shortly after that, I was invited by my friend, David Bez, founder and author of *Salad Pride*, to open a restaurant and school in London, bringing plant-based education and cuisine under one roof. We opened Plant Hub and Academy in East London and the dream came to life.

Plant Academy is all about putting plants at the forefront, never using meat substitutes, thinking about which ingredients you use and why, learning about real honest cooking, mastering elevated plating and food styling, and communicating your message through the plate. Originally, we ran short courses, but the main event was our week-long signature course called 'Plant 123' which I designed with Carolina Chinea (who features in the Stocks & Sauces chapter of this book, page 22). This course started with Plant One, the course in plant food fundamentals, Plant Two, the course in creativity and food design, and Plant Three, the course in plant-based business. All the courses were filled with the most fantastic array of international students, travelling to learn with us from every continent. We grew and evolved the program over the years and when the Covid pandemic hit, I reimagined the curriculum and spent three years filming Plant 123 online courses which live on today (you can find them at plantacademy.co.uk).

Having taught plant-based food around the world for the last decade I have heard every question under the sun but I have found that the same questions always pop up when people are trying to understand the unique art of plant-based cooking, questions such as 'Do I need to add water to my nut butter to help it blend?', 'How can I make this recipe quicker?', and 'Why do I have to soak nuts to make milk?'. All of these (and many more) will be answered within these pages.

MY PERSONAL PLATE

Like most of us in the West, I grew up eating a pretty normal diet of the time: bowls of cereal for breakfast, school lunches, big-brand confectionery, cinema sweets, ready meals and bottled salad dressings. Growing up in rural Devon and Somerset, however, I was lucky that this diet was always complemented with things my family or neighbours were growing, and I had people around me who liked to cook.

When I was small, I always opted for no butter on my sandwiches and roast dinners without the meat, not because of any dietary choice I was making but because it was just what I liked. My mum had gone off meat when she was pregnant with me and I'm convinced this was a sign of what was to come!

At three or four years old I declared that I was vegan. My mum had no idea where I had got this concept from, innocently packed me off to school with goat's cheese sandwiches, and it was forgotten about a week later, not to emerge again till two decades later when this plant-based idea put down its roots.

With a natural curiosity for food, I always liked to do things a bit differently. From as early

as I can remember I was devouring recipe books, and by the age of eight or nine I was making cupcakes and spice rubs for steaks. I unusually loved the fishmongers and butchers' shops and always keen to try the most adventurous things possible, that would make my parents squirm. At this time, I actually thought I might become a butcher when I grew up, as I was so fascinated with the way different cuts of meat were prepared.

By my early teens I was filleting fish, perfecting soufflés and making three-course school-night meals for my family and I, rooting through my Leiths or Mary Berry cookery books and intent on making every single dish. Even with this clear love and fascination for food it never occurred to me this could be a career option, so I went off to do fashion design and marketing at university. If you have read my book *Mind Food* you'll know what happened to my food relationship in this time; but in brief I lost someone I loved and ended up developing a concoction of eating disorders. I had a distorted relationship with food in my early twenties but continued to cook a lot for friends and family and started to join the dots between what food we ate and how it made us feel. This was just at the start of the wellness boom in the UK when cookery books like *Honestly Healthy* by Natasha Corrett and Vicki Edgson first came out, which linked food with lifestyle and introduced ingredients like avocados and goji berries to me. These plant-based foods opened up a whole new way of eating that reignited my passion for food and I will always credit them, alongside the support of my family and some wonderful alternative therapies, for my monumental recovery from being almost sectioned to becoming a passionate foodie once more.

By the time I was finishing my degree I was eating almost everything once more but had realized from being so unwell that I could no longer tolerate gluten and dairy. I have had a lifelong aversion to eggs (even the smell makes me sick!), and was just eating some meat and fish. I had created my own whole food, mostly plant-based, way of eating and seen the power of this transforming my own mental health. So, after five years of art school, fashion design and marketing, I pivoted and dove feet first into the food world, getting every job in the industry that I could find, from working at organic farm shops, to the local pub (which had a vegan menu), doing social media for a wellness centre and working for a local charity supporting adults with mental health challenges to work in food.

I was extremely fortunate with the people I met during that time, and everything suddenly seemed to realign. The connection that changed the course of my career and plate was with Kate Lewis, the creator of Asparagasm, London's first experiential vegan and gluten-free supper club. She would collaborate with classical chefs and challenge them to make vegan and gluten-free menus – her strapline was 'No fucking risotto!' and the Asparagasm logo was a cowgirl riding a bunch of asparagus. As soon as I heard the name of her business, I was in. I worked at her pub and dreamt of being involved in her mind-blowing dinner experiences, then one day she called me to ask if I could help her open a permanent venue for Asparagasm in the Cotswolds. I dropped everything and took the role of manager.

At this moment, I decided to give the vegan thing a go. We spent six months setting up the restaurant and I was learning everything I could

about the vegan way of life. Within weeks of us opening the head chef left and I took the role overnight. This opportunity led to years of Asparagasm recipes and events and led me to everything I do today.

I had already been accustomed to years of unusual food requests due to my eating disorders, but now in not only being vegan, but also creating recipes in the kitchen, there was something familiar about starting to order, cook and create in this new way. However, this time it felt extremely empowering, especially as people were just starting to understand better and offer more food options for vegans.

What started out 12 years ago as a lifestyle to support my mental health and went on to be influenced by a career change, eventually ended up, after years in the industry, to be a more revolutionary way of life. I now still eat vegan and mostly gluten-free, and after years of gut healing I can finally tolerate more challenging ingredients. I like to think of my current plate as my own form of activism, challenging the norm, boycotting big brands and actively using my art to communicate what is possible through how we choose to eat.

THE REAL FOOD REVOLUTION

Long-time vegans might remember the risottos and stuffed mushrooms of the past, or recall being sat at a table with pathetic-looking salads while being surrounded by feasting friends and unapproving family members. While that experience may still exist, the plant based way of life is more commonly accepted and now often seen as a trailblazing trend.

There are many reasons for eating plant-based meals, ranging from health benefits, ethical concerns, animal cruelty, religion and even politics, and I strongly believe we all must accept that eating more plants is the only way forward. The issue now is that 'plant based' options often consist of fake meats and junk foods which I would suggest should not be the focus of this category.

These ultra-processed foods may claim to have sustainable credentials, but they will never rival whole foods. I think of them as their own category of 'transition foods', foods that help people eat less actual meat and, for some plant-based eaters, help to satiate a craving or serve as a fun treat, but long-term they are not sustainable for our bodies or the planet.

The way forward is to educate people how to cook and eat a biodiverse plant-based diet that aligns with their local agriculture. I am not saying that every single person needs to be vegan, but if all of us could prioritize non-industrialized foods it would make a monumental impact.

We can all have a positive effect on the future of food and lead by example, and now you have this book in your hands there is no reason why you too can't start today, decision by decision, plate by plate, conversation by conversation, transforming the way you cook and eat.

THE PLANT ACADEMY ETHOS

These are the Plant Academy values to consider when cooking, eating and creating.

NATURAL
Plant Academy is about using whole food ingredients, by that I mean ingredients as close to their natural form as possible.

We combine these ingredients to make recipes, enhance them through fermentation, change their textures through cooking and evolve their flavours through techniques such as smoking, always with the mission of letting the ingredients speak for themselves.

HONEST
You won't find any ingredients pretending to be something else on any Plant Academy plate, but you might find cultural inspiration for a flavour or technique that we can put into action to tell stories through the dishes we make.

CONSCIOUS
We are conscious of cooking with a balance of ingredients and not overusing one particular thing (ahem... avocado, quinoa and cashew!) but making sure biodiversity is at the heart of what we do.

SEASONAL
This is a book of techniques, base recipes and more complete recipes that use those techniques. All these recipes use mostly staple ingredients and I have provided seasonal suggestions where needed.

PLANT EMPOWERED
This way of cooking isn't restricted or regimented but with these tools you should feel empowered to make conscious choices about how to use the ideas in this book in your own cooking environment.

THE PILLARS OF PLANT FOOD

When I was thinking about the concept for this book, I realized that the pillars for plant-based foods of the future are: mushrooms, beans, adaptogens and seeds. At least one of these ingredients will feature in most of the recipes and techniques in some way. They stand ahead of their plant peers for supporting the health of our plates and our planet.

MUSHROOMS

In recent years mycelium have been a hot topic, from the world of medicinal mushrooms (which we will cover in the adaptogens chapter on page 135), to psychedelics and the ones we will be talking about here – culinary mushrooms. Mushrooms have the potential to bring the most unique texture to our plates: they can be barbecued, marinated and even squashed to make a centrepiece, and aside from their culinary credentials they grow without effort, can be sustainably cultivated and offer nutrition like nothing else. Medicinal mushrooms are said to boast incredibly supportive properties such as regenerating nerves in the gut and brain (lions mane), giving us energy by helping our bodies to better use oxygen (cordyceps) and supporting our digestive systems by regulating the gut microbiota. From the medicinal to the mainstream, all mushrooms truly are a food we can rely on to shape our plates now and in the future.

BEANS

At the time of writing, beans are being championed by the UN as an ingredient for our future. Their aim is that there is a bean option on every menu alongside your usual meat, fish and vegetarian dish. Beans are essential for the health of our planet as they fix nitrogen in the soil. They are also a great source of fibre which is often missing from our Western diets. Beans are not only delicious in their own right, but can be used to thicken sauces, form the base for ice creams and even be baked into cakes.

ADAPTOGENS

The missing link in our modern healthcare systems are adaptogens, a powerful group of plants that adapt to their surroundings, each with their own unique benefits. The essential ingredients grow in challenging climates and are sought after for their reported effects in supporting our health and particular benefits, such as maca for libido and enegy, ashwagandha for stress management, and mushrooms including reishi for their potential to ward off disease in the body. There is no reason that these ingredients shouldn't be commonplace in our kitchens, as they offer the benefit of being your personal at-home apothecary. This is something you will learn to cultivate as you read this book.

SEEDS

The sustainable sisters of our overused nut friends, seeds have the benefit of being exceptionally easy to grow and lighter on a digestive system. Pumpkin, sunflower, chia, sesame and hemp all have their unique benefits and flavour profiles, yet are often less popular than nuts. The next century will no doubt see a seed revolution (on many levels) especially as we all embrace seeds grown closer to home.

PEACE AND PLANTS, PLANT ACADEMY

BEFORE YOU BEGIN

The following pages contain some key information that will help you carry out the techniques and recipes in this book.

HOW TO USE A BLENDER

This may sound like an unnecessary thing to write about; but trust me, using a blender isn't as easy as you may think. I have seen many blenders broken, abused and misused, so here are some rules for best practice.

KNOW YOUR EQUIPMENT

A blender is not a food processor or a Thermomix, these are entirely different machines for different jobs. A blender is a high-powered machine with a machine base and removable jug with a blade at the bottom and lots of space for blending. It is designed for making things smooth and is the ideal candidate for making creams, milks, dips and flours.

GET COMFORTABLE

Set up your blender near the front of your workspace or countertop. Make sure it is flat on the surface, directly in front of you and not going to slip and slide around. Be careful that you are not leaning over something to get to the blender.

LOADING

If you are using small ingredients such as chia seeds or spices, be sure to add them to the blender last to avoid them getting stuck around the blade at the bottom.

When making anything with a setting agent (such as a cheesecake cream with coconut oil and cacao butter), blend the mixture without the setting agent until smooth, and stream in the setting agent at the end. This stops the oils from going rancid as a result of over blending and ensures they are emulsified through the mixture for smooth and set end result.

BE PATIENT

There's nothing worse than a lumpy cream, plant-based or otherwise! Be patient with what you are blending. If it seems like nothing is happening, you most likely need more liquid or a slower speed.

DON'T ATTACK

There seems to be a universal urge to be rather heavy handed with a blender tamper, prodding and poking the mixture you are blending. Use the tamper to help the mixture to move, but as soon as it is moving either hold the tamper angled to the side of the blender jug or remove it and add the stopper to the lid. The tamper is most useful to push down mixture at the sides or help a thicker mixture get moving. Please don't use a spatula instead of a tamper!

THE VORTEX

When making anything the consistency of single or double cream, you should ideally create a vortex with the mixture. This is when the mixture is blending without intervention and you can see a cross shape and passage in the centre where the mixture is moving. When the blender is in this state you are sure to create a smooth end result.

OFF AND ON

Always set the blender back to the lowest speed and off high-power mode when you have finished so you (or someone else) doesn't get a surprise next time they use it. Not following this step normally involves someone being covered in whatever they were about to blend.

HOW TO USE A DEHYDRATOR

A dehydrator, known as the 'oven' of raw cuisine, is used to slow-dry food with gentle heat over a long period, preserving nutrients and locking in flavours. The benefits of using a dehydrator include being able to create unique textures without cooking, enhance the flavours of ingredients (for example dried tomatoes) and reduce waste in the kitchen by drying anything that is no longer needed (for example pulp from juices or nut milks).

In gourmet raw food and now in many creative kitchens, you will see dehydrators used to make vegetable powders, wraps, 'glass', crackers and candies, to warm up sauces and creams and to ferment cheeses, among many other uses.

These are some key tips for using a dehydrator:

- Make sure that you have the right temperature and time required.
- Make sure that foods are 95% dehydrated.
- Prepare items together that require the same temperature and mostly the same time. Do not place savoury and sweet foods in the dehydrator at the same time as they will become contaminated.
- Place dried foods in a dark, cool and dry area.

- Once your food is dehydrated, allow it to cool to room temperature to avoid condensation inside packaging.
- For better results and a long shelf life, consider using a vacuum sealer to package dehydrated food for storage.

FOUNDATIONAL KNIFE SKILLS

Knives are essential tools in any kitchen. Handled properly, they are an extension of the chef's hand. Mishandled, they can cause serious injury. Here are some key pieces of advice for selecting and handling knives.

- Every chef should own three knives: an 8-inch chef's knife (see page 19), with a slight curve to the blade, ideal for dicing and chopping; a paring knife, to trim and peel fruits and vegetables, slice small items and make precise cuts; and a bread knife, useful for cutting produce with thick skin like tomatoes and aubergines.
- Store all knives in the provided knife block or magnetic knife rack, not in a drawer.
- Wash all knives by hand and dry immediately with a soft cloth. Never let any acidic residues sit on the blade.
- Only use your knife on the chopping board – wood, bamboo, polypropylene and acrylic boards are all excellent choices.
- Sharpen your knives a few times a year using water stone, whetstone or an electronic knife sharpener.
- Make sure your hands are dry and the surface on which you work is non-slip.

AN INTRODUCTION TO FOOD PREP TERMINOLOGY

JULIENNE To cut into matchstick-size pieces, usually about 5 cm (2 inch) long and 3 mm (⅛ inch) thick.

BRUNOISE Perfect cubes, made from a julienne.

MINCED To cut into 3mm (⅛ inch) pieces or smaller.

CHOPPED FINE To cut into 3–6 mm (⅛–¼ inch) pieces.

SLICED To cut into pieces with two flat edges (the thickness of the slices will depend on the recipe).

DICED To cut into uniform cubes (the size of the dice will depend on the recipe).

HOW TO DICE AN ONION
Start by cutting off the tip, opposite to the root end. You want to keep the root system intact since it aids in keeping the vegetable together as you cut it, making it easier to handle.

Cut the onion in two halves lengthwise. Peel the onion, and then place the flat, cut side facing down. Cut several layers, horizontally, into the onion, all the way to the root system, but do not cut all the way through the root end. The number of cuts depends on the size of the onion and the desired size of the chop or dice.

Then, with the tip of your knife, make several vertical cuts, pole to pole, being careful not to cut all the way through the root end. Slice using your knuckles as a guide for the knife while holding the onion with your fingertips. Pull your fingertips in towards your palm, extending the knuckles outward when cutting for more control.

Be sure to keep the cut sides of the onion face down as much as possible. This reduces tears from those ruptured cell walls being more exposed to the air.

HOW TO MINCE A GARLIC CLOVE
Use the side of your knife to give the garlic clove a quick rap or two. This is enough pressure to crack the peel, and it should come off the clove easily. Trim off any woody stem.

Using a chef's or paring knife, begin making vertical cuts lengthwise through the garlic clove, spacing each cut less than 3mm (⅛ inch) apart. Now rotate the garlic clove 90 degrees, and slice across the previous cuts. Again, space the cuts less than 3mm (⅛ inch) apart.

Rock the knife back and forth over the pile of minced garlic, re-gathering the garlic into a pile as needed, until the garlic is finely minced.

HOW TO PICK AND CUT HERBS
PICKING SOFT HERBS Unless you are blending herbs, avoid using the stems. Pick the leaves by gently pushing them off the stem. Lightly rinse and pat dry before chopping.

PICKING HEARTY HERBS For herbs like rosemary, remove the leaves by sliding your thumb and index finger down the stalk against the grain.

CHOPPING HERBS 'CHIFFONADE' Bunch up the leaves in a tight pile. Hold the pile with your non-dominant hand, slice through it with a sharp knife. Keep the blade flush against the hand holding the pile.

STOCKS & SAUCES

THE SECRET INGREDIENT IS TIME

By Carolina Chinea

Food consultant, food designer & creative trainer

In the intricate dance of culinary creation, the distinction between a lacklustre dish and one that sings with satisfaction lies in the artful process of layering flavours and the pursuit of perfect balance. This chapter is a journey into the transformative alchemy of cooking, where common and humble ingredients are elevated to extraordinary heights through the infusion of time and the mindful constructions of stocks and sauces – two important foundation blocks in any culinary adventure.

Why the deep affection for stocks and sauces? Not just culinary options, they are secret weapons for elevating the taste profiles of our dishes. We are committed to crafting meals that not only tantalize the taste buds but also possess depth and character, especially in plant-based cuisine.

Stocks lay the very foundation of a cuisine, serving as its backbone. Here is your first lesson: the art of layering flavours.

Sauces, on the other hand, possess the transformative ability to elevate any dish, adding appeal, complexity and sheer tastiness. They are the crowning glory, turning the mundane into the magnificent. Lesson two: achieving balance and understanding consistency.

This chapter is a celebration of these aromatic wonders – the simmering stews, hearty soups and luscious sauces that infuse our kitchens with warmth and fragrance. So irresistible are their aromas that a mere moment's absence finds the air saturated with their tantalizing scents, and the anticipation of culinary delights rises like the mercury in a thermometer, wishing for a storm to complete the sensory experience.

In the art of gastronomy, time is is an essential ingredient, woven into the fabric of our creations. Making stocks, sauces and soups is indeed a slow business, demanding hours to coax out the flavours and transform humble components into culinary treasures. And in this act of culinary generosity, we find the essence of pleasure, as Brillat-Savarin so beautifully articulated in *The Physiology of Taste*:

'Inviting a person to dine with us is to take charge of his happiness for as long as he is under our roof.'

Happiness begins in this chapter. How do we measure time in the kitchen? With the spoon. As food critic Hannah Goldfield observed, spoons are instruments of peace, inviting harmony and delight with each gentle stir.

So, grab your spoon and join me on a culinary journey where time is the most valuable ingredient of all. In the following pages, we'll explore the art of stock-making, sauce-simmering and flavour-building, uncovering the joys of cooking with patience, passion and a bit of magic.

'If you are not capable of a bit of witchcraft, don't trouble yourself with cooking.'

Sidonie-Gabrielle Colette (French novelist)

ESSENTIAL STOCKS & SAUCES

TECHNIQUE 1: ENHANCE

LIGHT STOCK

Homemade stock takes some planning and preparation; however, it's worth the effort as you can prepare large quantities and store some for later use. This light vegetable stock is translucent in colour and can be used anywhere you want to add a light flavour but not overpower, just like when using a stock cube. It can form the base for several dishes, including cooking grains and making soups.

Makes: About 1 litre (34fl oz/1 quart/4–5 cups)

Time taken: 3–4 hours

2 medium white onions, peeled and finely
    sliced
2 small carrots, roughly chopped
1 leek, green part only, washed and roughly
    sliced
2 celery stalks, roughly chopped
1 fennel bulb, roughly chopped
2 garlic cloves, with the skin on and just bashed
    to open
½ tsp black peppercorns
1 bay leaf
3 litres (100fl oz/12½ cups) filtered water
1 thyme sprig
10g (⅓oz) flat-leaf parsley leaves

From cold, put all the ingredients (except the thyme and parsley) in the water in a large saucepan, and bring to the boil. Simmer over a low heat, with the lid on, for at least 45 minutes, and up to a maximum of 2 hours.

Remove from the heat and add the herbs to infuse the flavours. Cover and let it rest for 1 more hour and then strain carefully.

Cool completely, then store it in an airtight container in the fridge for up to 4 days or in ice-cube trays in the freezer for up to 1 month.

TIP – Remember to always wash vegetables before you use them.

TECHNIQUE 2: ENRICH

DARK STOCK

We often think of stocks as being rich because they are made of meat but this recipe gives you a complex and deep end result with the use of vegetables, mushrooms, wine and seaweed. It's ideal for using as a base for stews and rice dishes.

Makes: About 1 litre (34fl oz/1 quart/4–5 cups)
Time taken: 2 hours

50ml (1½fl oz/3½ tbsp) olive oil

3 onions, peeled and finely diced

½ tsp sea salt

75ml (2½fl oz/5 tbsp) tamari

200ml (7fl oz/scant 1 cup) vegan red wine

100g (3½oz) tomato, grated

2 tbsp tomato purée

10g (⅓oz) harissa paste (optional)

1 leek, green part only, washed and roughly
  sliced

2 garlic cloves, bashed (with skin on)

2 medium potatoes, washed and cut into 1cm
  cubes

150g (5½oz) fresh shiitake mushrooms, finely
  sliced

10g (⅓oz) dried shiitake or cep mushrooms

3 litres (100fl oz/12½ cups) filtered water

1 strip kombu

2 rosemary sprigs

1 thyme sprig

Heat the oil in a large saucepan over a medium heat, add the onions and salt and cook for 10 minutes, stirring regularly, until the onions are starting to colour and caramelize. Add 1 tablespoon of the tamari and stir, then add 50ml (1½fl oz/3½ tbsp) of the red wine and stir until the liquid has evaporated. Repeat this process 3 times.

Add the tomato, tomato purée and harissa paste (if using) and cook for 2–3 minutes until the liquid disappears. Add the leek, garlic cloves, potatoes and mushrooms and cook for at least 15–20 minutes until well browned.

Add the water and kombu, bring to the boil, then reduce the heat and simmer for 40 minutes to a maximum of 2 hours, with the lid on. The longer the time, the richer the stock, but do keep an eye on it as it cooks. It will be good after 40 minutes but even better and richer in flavour after 2 hours. Turn off the heat and add the herbs to infuse the flavours. Let it rest, covered, for 30 minutes then strain carefully.

Keep it in an airtight container in the fridge for up to 4 days or in ice-cube trays in the freezer for up to 3 months.

SMOKED DASHI

Dashi is a deceptively simple, clear broth from Japan made with seaweed, bento (dried tuna flakes) and water, which produces a liquid with maximum umami. In this plant-based version we use shiitake mushrooms and lapsang souchong tea which has an equally interesting flavour as bento dashis and can be used in soups and for cooking grains. Try different teas for interesting variations on this recipe.

Makes: 400ml (14fl oz/1¾ cups)

Time taken: 30 minutes, plus 6 hours soaking time

40g (1½oz) dried kombu seaweed	2 litres (68fl oz/8½ cups) filtered water
2 sheets nori seaweed	1 tsp lapsang souchong tea leaves
5–6 large dried shiitake mushrooms	

Add all of the ingredients, apart from the lapsang souchong tea, to a jar and soak in the fridge overnight or for at least 6 hours.

The next day, add the mixture to a pan and bring just to a simmer for 5 minutes, not above 115°C/175°F (you can use a thermometer to ensure this). Then turn off the heat, add the tea leaves and let it cool again.

Strain the liquid from the solids* and use straight away, store in the fridge for up to 5 days or freeze in ice-cube trays for up to 1 month.

*Try the seaweed and mushrooms in salads or soups.

GLACE

A glace or demi-glace is an intense, glossy, thick sauce. Glaces are the more concentrated option and both can be used to add a wonderful richness to a dish. When cooking with plants it is these kinds of flavours that can create so much satisfaction and surprise. This technique can be used for light and dark stocks and involves using chickpeas to help thicken the stock. You can roast leftover chickpeas with oil or toss them through salads enhancing another dish.

Makes: 300ml (10fl oz/1¼ cups)

Time taken: 2 hours, plus overnight soaking

1 litre (34fl oz/4¼ cups) dark stock	75g (2½oz) dried chickpeas (garbanzo beans), soaked overnight in filtered water then rinsed

Pour the stock into a medium or small saucepan, add the soaked and rinsed chickpeas and cook on a low heat, stirring often, for 1 hour.

Remove from the heat, leave uncovered to rest for 30 minutes, then remove the chickpeas with a slotted spoon and set aside. Place the stock back over the heat and simmer until reduced by two-thirds – it should be a thickened and glossy sauce.

Cool the sauce completely and store it in the fridge for up to 3 days. Warm before serving.

FLAVOUR BALANCE

Alongside technique, the most important part of cooking is flavour. I have found that, especially with plant-based food, we can get a little lost in the plate styling and forget true flavour.

Flavour balance comes into action in every part of the cooking process, from the initial cooking of a vegetable to a more complex sauce and then layering different components together. It's just as important with raw dishes such as salads. Without understanding flavour, we can't even start to build a dish.

Do not confuse flavour with taste, which is a physical sensation like smell, sight and touch. Flavour is taste + memory, smell, texture, surroundings and even company. A dictionary definition of flavour as 'a distinctive quality or atmosphere; suggestion: a poem with a Shakespearean flavour', which is a great way to explain it.

You can read more about taste when we talk about the five (or seven) tastes that come together to make a balanced recipe, see below. In the context of plating, flavour is the most important part, as placing components together tells their story, and their relative proportions and placement explain your intention and creates the overall experience of the dish.

Understanding flavour balance is a crucial part of cooking. Knowing how to enhance, evolve or tone down a flavour is done through appreciating the different tastes and how they affect each other. In most dishes, all of these elements play a part and once you are familiar with each one you can start to bring balance and excitement to your cooking.

TASTES

Sweet
Here to bring balance to overly salty, sour or even spicy foods. Ingredients such as honey, maple syrup and dates can help stronger flavours feel more palatable.

Salty
Salt is not just about making things salty but enhancing the flavour of a dish. Using salt in desserts, for example, will bring out the other flavours rather than making salty desserts. Salt can be found in many places other than salt, such as tamari, miso, fermented brine, and celery.

Sour
From citrus fruit to vinegar, sour elements cut through sweet, fatty or salty foods to bring balance.

Bitter
Once you appreciate bitter foods your palate expands in a new way. Leafy greens such as rocket and chicory are a great example of bitter foods that can help cut through the richness of a dish and offer balance.

Umami
The complex savoury flavour we often desire, umami comes from soy sauce, mushrooms, miso and sometimes fermented foods. It's often the missing element in a dish that doesn't quite feel finished.

Fat
It may seem unusual to list fat as a flavour, but it is key in transporting tastes through our mouths. Fat gives food a more rounded mouthfeel and texture: think of a salad with dressing or greens cooked in olive oil.

Pungent
Ingredients such as raw onions and garlic give foods a pungent taste (although they sweeten when cooked). Without other flavours this can be overwhelming but when paired with a salty or creamy dressing, the strength of flavour will come into balance.

Kokumi
The newest taste, a Japanese word to describe 'richness'. This taste is more of a sensation than a flavour, and can be used to describe foods such as slow-roasted ingredients, kokumi being the part that heightens the other flavours and gives 'roundness' of taste.

DRESSINGS

The idea with these dressings is that they form a base recipe to carry any flavours, and the most important thing is to understand the various techniques that make a cohesive, flavourful base.

You'll notice I almost always use olive oil. I think the negative effects of sunflower oil outweigh its benefit of being neutral in flavour. With olive oil you can access stronger or more neutral flavours and explore which ones work for you.

INFUSED

Infusing can apply to anything from herbs and teas to stocks and sauces. In the context of dressings, I use two techniques: hot and cold oil infusions.

BASE RECIPE

PARSLEY OIL (COLD INFUSION)

This oil is just one example of making a herb oil in a blender. Parsley makes a vibrant green oil but you can mix and match many different herbs - try shiso, basil or coriander, for example.

Makes: 500ml (17fl oz/about 2 cups)
Time taken: 30 minutes

100g (3½oz) Flat-leaf parsley leaves and stems, chopped

400ml (14fl oz/1¾ cups) light olive oil
1 tsp sea salt

Equipment
High-powered blender
Fine-mesh sieve

Prepare a bowl of iced filtered water and place a metal bowl on the top.

Put the chopped parsley and oil in the blender and blend until you have a bright green, smooth oil – the oil may be hot if it takes your blender a few minutes to create a smooth mixture.

Wipe the cold metal bowl so it is dry and still over the ice and transfer the green oil to the cold bowl. Leave to cool completely and add the salt.

Strain the oil through a fine-mesh sieve, letting it slowly drip into another bowl and being careful not to squeeze it as you will affect the colour.

Store in a sealed container in the fridge for up to 1 week. You can make a pesto with the pulp or add to any cooking as a delicious herby accent.

SPICE OIL (HOT & STRAINED INFUSION)

This spice oil is featured in recipes such as the BBQ sauce on page 84. You can try all sorts of different spice combinations and use this oil in combination with other ingredients to make a dressing.

Makes: 250ml (8fl oz/1 cup)
Time taken: 50 minutes

250ml (8¾fl oz/1 cup) olive oil
2 cloves
5 green cardamom pods
1 tsp fennel seeds
1 star anise
3 black peppercorns

Equipment
Fine-mesh sieve

Put all the ingredients in a saucepan and slowly bring to a simmer. Simmer over a medium–low heat for 10 minutes – you want to heat the oil for long enough to extract the flavours but not burn the spices. Turn off the heat, leave for a further 30 minutes to infuse and cool completely.

Strain the spices from the oil using a fine-mesh sieve and store in a sealed glass container or sauce bottle at room temperature for up to 1 week.

SMOKED SALSA MACHA (HOT INFUSION)

Salsa macha is a wonderful Mexican chilli oil, commonly found on café tables in Mexico as a condiment to spice up any dish. This recipe is slightly less refined than the other oils and instead leaves the chilli flakes in to make a fantastically flavoured end result.

Makes: 300ml (10fl oz/1¼ cups)
Time taken: 30 minutes

250ml (8¾fl oz/1 cup) olive oil
1–2 tbsp dried chilli (pepper) flakes (you can use red chilli flakes or a mixture of ancho/ habanero etc., depending on your spice goal and what you have access to)
2 tbsp smoked paprika
1 tbsp smoked sweet paprika
1 tbsp smoked sea salt
1–2 tsp coconut sugar
Secret ingredient: 2 tbsp nori flakes (optional)

Put all the ingredients, apart from seaweed (if using), in a saucepan and slowly bring to a simmer over a medium heat. Once simmering, turn off the heat, add the seaweed (if using) and leave to infuse and cool completely.

Do not strain. Simply transfer to a sealed glass container or sauce bottle and keep at room temperature for up to 1 month.

EMULSIFIED

Emulsifying means to combine two ingredients together in a stable mixture that wouldn't normally combine. Often this involves mixing oil and another liquid. By using a mixture of different emulsifiers, you can stabilize a dressing or sauce to create a thicker texture.

BASE RECIPE

MISO & MUSTARD VINAIGRETTE

A classic vinaigrette is an example of emulsification. It usually involves using lemon, oil and mustard – the mustard is the stabilizer in this case. This dressing is a little more funky with the addition of miso.

Makes: 200ml (7fl oz/1 scant cup)
Time taken: 10 minutes

150ml (5fl oz/⅔ cup) olive oil
3 tbsp lemon juice
1 tbsp Dijon mustard
1 tsp miso (white ideally, but you can also use brown)
½–1 tsp honey or agave (to taste)
¼ tsp sea salt (as needed depending on the saltiness of your miso)

Put all the ingredients in a jar and shake vigorously to combine, alternatively whisk or blend them together. Store in a sealed glass jar in the fridge until ready to serve.

BASE RECIPE

AQUAFABA MAYO

Aquafaba is the water leftover from cooking beans and legumes, most commonly chickpeas, and butter and white beans. Because of its high protein content, it works like egg whites to emulsify and thicken and can be used to make a delicious mayonnaise-style dressing. While you can also use soy milk or cashew cream for this, aquafaba is fantastic as it would otherwise go to waste. It has a neutral flavour and works wonderfully. I use olive oil as the end result is delicious.

Makes: 400ml (14fl oz/1¾cups)
Time taken: 20 minutes

100ml (3½fl oz/scant ½ cup) aquafaba
300ml (10fl oz/1¼ cups) extra virgin olive oil
1 tbsp lemon juice
2 tsp apple cider vinegar
1 tsp sea salt
Dried chilli (pepper) flakes, lime or lemon zest or smoked sea salt (optional)

Equipment
High-powered blender

Put the aquafaba in a blender that has a lid with a funnel into which you can stream in the oil (if you don't have this, use a stick blender). Start to blend and as the aquafaba becomes slightly aerated and lighter in colour very gradually stream in the oil and continue to blend on a low speed and eventually the mixture will become very thick. Add and blend the lemon juice, apple cider vinegar, salt and any other seasonings. Store in a sealed container in the fridge for up to 5 days.

CREAMY

Creamy sauces are an essential part of plant-based food. They cut through strong flavours and add that enjoyable roundness to many plates. Often using nuts and seeds, these are just some examples of creamy sauce bases that I hope will inspire many more.

BASE RECIPE

TAHINI SAUCE

This simple tahini sauce is a great seed-based option for a creamy dressing. You can adjust the amount of water to make it more or less thick and, as with the cashew sour cream, adjust the flavours as you feel inspired to do.

Makes: 200ml (7fl oz/1 scant cup)

Time taken: 10 minutes

75g (2½oz) tahini
150ml (5fl oz/⅔ cup) filtered water

1 tsp white miso, brown miso or ½ tsp sea salt
1 small red chilli, deseeded and finely chopped (optional)

Equipment (optional)
High-powered blender

Put all of the ingredients in a blender or mixing bowl and mix until thoroughly combined, to make a smooth thick mixture.

Transfer the mixture to a container, seal and store in the fridge for up to 4 days.

BASE RECIPE

CASHEW SOUR CREAM

This cashew sour cream is quite a staple in the Plant Academy kitchen because it is a fantastic creamy base recipe that can be used on so many different dishes, from a pop of cream on a spicy taco to a dressing for a creamy salad. Try making it with miso rather than salt, add smoked paprika, add chilli, or swap the oil here for an infused oil.

Makes: 550ml (18½fl oz/2⅓ cups)

Time taken: 20 minutes, plus optional fermenting time overnight

400g (14oz) fermented cashews (page 113) or 300g/10½oz cashews, soaked in just-boiled filtered water for 1 hour

100ml (3½fl oz/scant ½ cup) filtered water
2–3 tbsp lemon juice
1–2 tbsp apple cider vinegar
1 small garlic clove, peeled
½ tsp sea salt
100ml (3½fl oz/scant ½ cup) olive oil

Equipment
High-powered blender

If using un-fermented cashews, rinse and drain the cashews, tip them into the blender with the water and blend until totally smooth. Add the remaining ingredients to the smooth cashew mixture and blend once more until smooth. (If you're using fermented cashews, you can just put everything in the blender all at once.)

Transfer the cashew sour cream to a container, seal and store in the fridge for up to 4 days.

SAUCES

Creating any dish is an exercise in understanding and finding balance. On a plate you will balance flavours, textures and even colours. The sauce is the liquid element that will bring any dish together. It can add depth of flavour, in the case of a rich broth or intense glace; texture, in the case of a pesto or romesco; or simply a pop of colour, in the case of a pink cream or golden mayonnaise.

One of the classic ways to think about sauce was created by Auguste Escoffier, who created a system of 'mother' and 'daughter' sauces. You can read more about his work in his book *Le guide culinaire* (*A Guide to Modern Cookery*), which contains sauces thickened with a starch (like the Cashew Béchamel on page 47), body-thickened sauce (like the 'Mole' Blanco on page 83) and emulsions (as on pages 32-33). When you start to design dishes and analyze what kind of sauce you need, this way of thinking can be useful as it guides you through different techniques that explore not only thickness but also flavour and texture, as well as how to use these within a dish.

BASE RECIPE

SEED PESTO

A pesto is a classic sauce very commonly used on pasta but also as a salad dressing, an addition to a dish or even swirling through a cream. This is a simple plant-based pesto made using seeds with the addition of parsley and chilli as an enjoyable flavour lift.

Makes: 250ml (8¾fl oz/1 cup)

Time taken: 10 minutes

30g (1oz) flat-leaf parsley, roughly chopped

30g (1oz) basil, roughly torn

100g (3½oz) seeds, such as hemp, pumpkin or sunflower

Zest and juice of 1 lemon

½–1 tsp chilli (pepper) flakes (adjust depending on heat preference)

1 tbsp nutritional yeast

½ tsp sea salt

100ml (3½fl oz/scant ½ cup) extra virgin olive oil

Equipment

Food processor

Place the herbs into a food processor with half the seeds, the lemon zest and juice and seasonings. Pulse until well combined. Stream in the oil gradually.

When the ingredients are combined, add the second half of the seeds to keep some texture.

Store in a jar in the fridge for up to 1 week.

TIP – Explore toasting the seeds to enrich the flavour of your pesto.

HARISSA SAUCE

ROMESCO

Harissa is a north African pepper sauce made with chillies and used, traditionally, to give flavour to ingredients such as grains and vegetables. This is a pourable harissa that can be used to add spice to ingredients such as hummus or a cashew cream. You can also use it to give depth to stocks such as the dark stock on page 26, or add it to provide a dash of warmth to a variety of dishes.

A classic Catalan sauce used to give a Latin flare to many dishes. Made from roasted peppers, almonds and sometimes tomatoes with the addition of sherry vinegar and smoky paprika. Romesco can be served with delicious roasted vegetables, potatoes or anywhere where some sunny Mediterranean flavour is required.

Makes: 500ml (17fl oz/about 2 cups)
Time taken: 10 minutes

2 red (bell) peppers, deseeded and chopped
3 tbsp smoked paprika
1 tbsp sweet paprika
75ml (2½fl oz/5 tbsp) lemon juice
1 tbsp ground cumin
½ tsp ground coriander
1 tbsp freshly grated ginger
½ tsp red chilli (pepper) flakes
½ tsp cayenne pepper
½ tsp sea salt
200ml (7fl oz/scant 1 cup) olive oil

Equipment
High-powered blender
Fine-mesh sieve

Makes: 500ml (17fl oz/about 2 cups)
Time taken: 1 hour

2 red (bell) peppers
2 garlic cloves, peeled
50ml (1½fl oz/3½ tbsp) apple cider vinegar
2 tbsp sherry vinegar
2 tbsp smoked paprika
1 fresh red chilli, chopped and deseeded
180ml (6fl oz/¾ cup) olive oil
300g (10½oz) almonds, roasted

Equipment
Food processor

Put all the ingredients apart from the oil into a blender and start to blend.

Stream the olive oil into the blender while it is running slowly, and continue until the ingredients are well combined and the sauce is a vibrant red colour.

Strain through a fine mesh sieve. Keep the sauce in an airtight container in the fridge for up to 1 week.

Preheat the oven to 200°C fan/220°C/425°F/gas 7.

Place the peppers and garlic cloves in the oven and roast for 40 minutes until soft. Place the peppers in a bowl to cool and then peel off the skin, also removing the seeds and stem.

Process all the ingredients except the almonds and oil to combine. Stream in the oil gradually. Add the almonds and process, keeping in mind that you are looking for a 'crunchy' texture.

Keep in an airtight container in the fridge for up to 1 week.

NUTS & SEEDS

Nuts and seeds are a major pillar of plant-based foods. They not only add a wonderfully flavoursome element to any meal, but also crunch, creaminess, richness, and they can even make a sauce! Far beyond plain nut butters and store-bought milks, there is a world of possibilities that will expand your food horizons, offer optimum nutrition, save your pennies and amp up the flavour of your food.

Nuts and seeds are a great source of protein and fats, so on a plant-based plate they play a key role in satiation. Key for all food groups is understanding the wide range of varieties out there and knowing what to do with them. In the case of nuts and seeds – particularly given the increase in nut allergies – rather than just relying on a monocrop like peanuts and almonds, we can be using seeds to their full potential, they have so much tastiness to offer.

In this chapter you will learn how to master making your own nut butters, maximize your satisfaction through understanding crunch, embrace nutty flavours and, most importantly, milk a hemp seed!

A lesson before we begin: as you start to learn more about plant milks, creams and butters you will come across the word 'activation' – this comes from the Raw Food movement where we 'activate' nuts and seeds to receive their full benefits when we consume them. When you see the term 'activating' or 'activation' we are talking about soaking the nuts or seeds (to remove all of the things we don't want), rinsing and then drying them again to create a 'purer' and tastier end result. Raw foodies would 'dehydrate' these nuts and seeds but you can also slow-roast them to dry them out.

MILKS & CREAMS

Plant milks and creams are so easy to make – they take hardly any time, and cost very little, but offer optimum flavour. All basic nut and seed milks and creams involve just two ingredients, your chosen nut or seed and water. From there you can jazz up your plant milk in whatever way you desire.

When you use the nuts and seeds that need to be soaked it is important to rinse them well. When we soak them, they soften and in the soaking process the enzyme inhibitors and phytic acid that are there to protect the nuts or seeds, but aren't so great for us to ingest, are removed.

If you want to heat any of your creations, note that the higher-fat nuts and seeds, such as walnuts and hemp seeds, aren't so tolerant of heat and might split, so be mindful.

TECHNIQUE 1

PLANT MILK

Homemade plant milk is great – hopefully after making it once you will be hooked! You can play around with any nut and seed and explore the different flavours: each one lends itself to different drinks, recipes and flavour combinations. Once you start making plant milks, you will begin to see which one works for you. You can bake the leftover pulp into cakes, add it to homemade granola or freeze it.

Makes: 400ml (14fl oz/1¾ cups)

Time taken: 5 minutes, plus soaking time

100g (3½oz) nut/seed, soaked in filtered water and rinsed (see page 180 for timings)

400ml (14fl oz/1¾ cups) water, room temperature and filtered

Equipment
High-powered blender
Nut milk bag, clean tea towel or muslin (cheesecloth)

Blend your soaked and rinsed nuts or seeds with the water for at least 30 seconds at a high speed.

Prepare a clean bowl with your chosen strainer (i.e., nut milk bag) then pour the plant milk through the strainer and into the bowl. Squeeze the bag to remove all of the liquid then save the pulp in the fridge or freezer until you are ready to use it. Store in an airtight container in the fridge for up to 3 days.

FLAVOUR IDEAS

CHOCOLATE: 1 tbsp cacao powder, 1 tsp carob powder, 1 tbsp maple syrup, ¼ tsp smoked sea salt

MAGIC: ½ tsp maca powder, ½ tsp lion's mane

PLANT CREAM

The idea with this base recipe is that you can season it up to be savoury or sweet. Not ALL nuts and seeds will work as a cream. As a rule of thumb, harder nuts are less likely to make a good cream. The easiest nuts for making into creams are cashew, macadamia, hemp seed and pine nut. A milk is 1-part nuts/seeds to 3–4 parts water, a single cream would be a 1:2–3 ratio nuts/seeds to water, and a double cream 1:1–1.5.

TIPS

– Tahini works as a great 1:1 alternative for cashews. You can also use coconut (fresh coconut or yoghurt), but you will need less water.

– Some nuts and seeds can be fermented to make an even more flavoursome and funky end result. Find out more about this process and how to create your own cheese on pages 112–113).

– A slight twist on this idea is to hot-smoke nuts or seeds in a stove-top smoker and instead of then soaking them, blend them with filtered water and olive oil. This makes a DELICIOUS smoky sauce that can be used on so many different plates.

For sweet Chantilly-style cream

Makes: 200g (7oz)

Time taken: 10 minutes, plus soaking time

100g (3½oz) cashews, soaked in filtered water for 4 hours or boiling water for 1 hour, and rinsed

100ml (3½fl oz/scant ½ cup) almond milk

2 tbsp maple syrup

Pinch of sea salt

½ tsp lemon juice

½ tsp vanilla extract, 1 tonka bean, grated or ½ tsp cinnamon, optional for flavour, or change the chosen plant milk to create different flavour variations

Equipment

High-powered blender

Blend all of the ingredients until silky smooth. Store in a sealed container in the fridge for up to 5 days.

For savoury cream

Makes: 400g (14oz)

Time taken: 10 minutes, plus soaking time

150g (3½oz) cashews, soaked in filtered water for 4 hours or boiling water for 1 hour

200ml (7fl oz/scant 1 cup) filtered water

1 tbsp white miso

50ml (1½fl oz/3½tbsp) olive oil

Equipment

High-powered blender

Blend all the ingredients until silky smooth. Store in a sealed container in the fridge for up to 4 days.

CRUNCH & CANDY

Nuts are mostly known as a crunchy and satisfying snack, and for adding that all-important crunch to a variety of dishes such as walnuts in a Waldorf salad or candied peanuts in a Balinese nasi campur. A great way to make everything you eat more satisfying is to make it crunch! So, here is a great base recipe for any nuts and seeds you'd like to add to your dishes. This recipe is for nut and seed candies, the ideal snack or topping for any occasion.

Makes: 300g (10½oz)
Time taken: 50 minutes

200g (7oz) any nuts, seeds or cacao nibs, ideally soaked for the correct soaking time in filtered water (see pages 180–183 for timings), then rinsed
50ml (1½fl oz/3½ tbsp) olive oil
2 tbsp maple syrup
½ tsp sea salt

Preheat the oven to 180°C fan/200°C/400°F/gas 6.

Combine your chosen soaked and rinsed nuts or seeds with the olive oil, maple syrup and salt in a large mixing bowl. The oil creates a great marinade and the maple syrup make the nuts or seeds extra crunchy. Spread the nuts and seeds out on a baking tray, either lined with a silicone baking sheet or not lined at all (as paper will stick). Bake for 20–40 minutes until golden. The smaller the seed, the less time they'll take to become golden.

Remove from the oven and leave to cool completely. Store in a sealed container at room temperature for up to 1 month.

OTHER FLAVOUR IDEAS

THE UMAMI ONE: Replace the salt with 1 tsp tamari

THE SMOKY ONE: Add ½ tsp smoked paprika and replace the salt for smoked sea salt

THE HERBY ONE: Add ½ tsp fennel seeds and ½ tsp dried oregano

THE SPICY ONE: Add ½ tsp dried chilli (pepper) flakes and ¼–½ chilli powder

NUT & SEED BUTTERS

Nut butters are simple to make and you can be incredibly creative. You can make a nutritionally potent activated walnut butter, and roast 30–50g (1–1¾oz) of these nuts to get a richer flavour; you could make a caramel-like butter from candied pecans, or combine nuts or seeds, such as mixing candied pumpkin seed with raw hemp seed butter. Use your creations on toast, in cakes and cookies, to thicken soups and much more!

Makes: 500g (1lb 2oz)
Time taken: 20 minutes

500g (1lb 2oz) raw/roasted/activated/candied
  nuts or seeds
Sea salt, to taste
1–2 tbsp olive oil (optional)

Equipment
Food processor

Process the nuts or seeds until they fully break down and start to bind together and continue to process until they have a completely smooth consistency. Patience is key and do persevere – when a clump of mixture forms eventually it will break down and become smooth. Add salt at the end, to taste, then add oil as needed, if the nuts really do need some help. Let the mixture cool completely and store in a sealed container or glass jar in the fridge for up to 1 month.

TIP – The ideal kit for making nut butter is a food processor. You can also use a blender but be prepared to be patient and keep scraping down the sides until you have your desired consistency, and stop if the mixture starts to get hot, as the nuts can go rancid when overheated.

A LESSON

When we talk about 'nut butters' like peanut and almond, which we are most familiar with, it is important to understand they are not the same as dairy butter or even a vegan butter. They do not melt and they most importantly contain no wet ingredients, but we use the word 'butter' as the final result is smooth and glossy like its dairy equivalent.

People can get confused with the difference between these milks, creams and butters but the key thing to remember in your nut butter making journey is that all ingredients must remain DRY. There is no soaking involved and if anything is wet in this process you will end up with a cream.

MILKS, CREAMS & BUTTERS

BLEND

MILK

CREAM

FERMENT *OR* FRESH

CHEESE

DON'T ADD WATER

CULTURED NUT BUTTER

NUT BUTTER

CHILLI, ROSEMARY & MOLASSES SEED LOAF

This seed loaf is laden with spice and seeds, and is a wonderful, easy gluten-free bake. Many versions exist, incorporating different combinations of similar ingredients, but it's a classic: a satiating and useful base recipe for you to adapt. You can try different combinations of spices and sweeteners but the key ratio to keep the same is the flax and chia seeds, which enable the loaf to bind.

Makes: 1 small loaf (12–15 slices)
Time taken: 1 hour 30 minutes

120g (4¼oz) shelled hemp seeds
100g (3½oz) gluten-free oats
100g (3½oz) pumpkin seeds
100g (3½oz) sunflower seeds
100g (3½oz) flax seeds, ground
100g (3½oz) chia seeds
30g (1oz) psyllium husks
2 tbsp chopped finely fresh or 1 tbsp chopped dried rosemary
1 tsp ancho chilli (pepper) flakes (or regular dried chilli flakes)
1 tsp sea salt
500ml (17fl oz/generous 2 cups) filtered water, room temperature, dashi or light stock
70ml (2½fl oz/⅓ cup) olive oil, plus extra for greasing
2 tbsp molasses

Equipment
450g (1lb) bread tin (silicone if you have it)

Put all the ingredients, except the water, oil and molasses, in a large bowl and mix to distribute the seeds evenly, then add the water, oil and molasses and stir to combine. Leave the mixture at room temperature to firm up for 30 minutes, until the liquid is mostly absorbed.

Preheat the oven to 170°C fan/190°C/375°F/gas 5.

Grease the bread tin with a little olive oil and then press the mixture into the prepared tin, pressing it down thoroughly so that there are no air pockets and the top is flat. Bake the loaf for 1 hour, until cooked through, then remove from the oven and allow it to cool in the tin for 10 minutes before transferring it to a rack to cool completely.

Keep whole in a sealed container at room temperature and cut as needed for up to 5 days, or slice and freeze in a sealed bag or container for up to 1 month.

TIP – You can turn this mixture into great crunchy seed crackers that are fantastic with the cheeseboard on page 119. Simply omit the psyllium husk and molasses and (after letting the mixture firm up for 30 minutes) spread the mixture 3–5mm (⅛–¼ inch) thick on a piece of baking paper on a baking tray or sheet, and bake at 180°C fan/200°C/400°F/gas 6 for about 40 minutes, or until crisp. These crackers can include up to 100g (3½oz) pulp from making nut or seed milks, root vegetable pulp from juicing, and so much more (no adjustments necessary). You can also switch up the spices using combinations like turmeric and chilli, leftover kimchi folded through the mix or smoked sea salt and smoked paprika.

CASHEW BÉCHAMEL TART

With Corn Pastry

This savoury tart is one of my lunchtime favourites. It has a creamy, smooth filling, crisp pastry and is perfect topped with fresh salad. A version of this recipe appeared in *Mind Food* and I often return to it with different nut and seed creams. You can replace the cashews with sunflower seeds for a more earthy flavour, make a green filling with pumpkin seeds and spinach folded through the mixture, or pine nuts for a richer flavour.

Makes: 1 large tart, serves 8-10
Time taken: 1 hour

For the corn pastry

100g (3½oz/¾ cup) white/yellow masa harina
150g (5oz/⅔ cup) chickpea (gram) flour
50g (1¾oz) potato flour
100g (3½oz) cold Vegan Butter (page 148), diced
50-70ml (¼ cup) cold filtered water
½ tsp smoked sea salt

For the cashew béchamel

2 tbsp olive oil
60g (2oz/½ cup) chickpea (gram) flour
500ml (17fl oz/generous 2 cups) Cashew Milk (page 38)
25g (¾oz) dijon mustard
1 tbsp nutritional yeast
1 tsp sea salt
¼ tsp freshly cracked black pepper
Pinch of freshly grated nutmeg

Equipment

20cm (8in) fluted tart tin with a removable base, lined with baking parchment

CORN PASTRY Preheat the oven to 180°C fan/200°C/400°F/gas 6. Toast the masa in a frying pan on a medium heat for 5 minutes until lightly golden. Allow to cool, then add it to the chickpea flour and potato flour in a large bowl. Add the butter then rub the flour and butter lightly between your fingertips until the mixture resembles breadcrumbs. Now add the water and salt and mix to form a dough. Be gentle with the pastry – you do not want to overwork it. Once a dough is formed, roll it into a round about 3–5mm (⅛–¼ inch) thick and carefully place into the lined tart tin. Fix any cracks with the extra pastry and press the pastry up to the sides of the tin neatening up the edges. Prick with a fork to avoid cracks and shrinkage, then bake in the oven for 15 minutes, until golden. Then remove from the oven and set aside to cool on a wire rack.

CASHEW BÉCHAMEL Heat the oil in a medium saucepan over a low heat then add the chickpea flour and whisk until combined. Gradually whisk in the cashew milk – the mixture should quickly thicken. Cook, whisking constantly, for 10 minutes, then add the mustard, nutritional yeast, salt, black pepper and nutmeg. Pour the mixture into the pastry shell, making sure the filling is even and smooth, then allow to cool.

Serve at room temperature or cool for around 30 minutes in the fridge before serving. Store in a sealed container in the fridge for up to 3 days.

TOPPING IDEAS

–Massaged Kale (page 48)
–Fresh tomato salad
–Fresh leaves and a zingy dressing
–Roasted roots

MASSAGED KALE

This simple and delicious recipe will revolutionize how you eat kale! One of my ULTIMATE pet peeves is being served raw kale – we can't digest it and, if you aren't used to eating raw plants, it could give you a stomach-ache. I think kale is made to be massaged and there is a special way to do this. I have roped all my friends and family members into this task and even the kale-averse have ended up falling for this way of eating it!

Serves: 2
Time taken: 10 minutes

1 bunch (about 200g/7oz) kale, washed and
　dried
3 tbsp cold-pressed oil, such as olive, pumpkin
　or hemp
1–2 tsp sea salt or tamari
1–2 tbsp Nut or Seed Butter (page 41), such as
　pumpkin seed, tahini, sunflower or cashew

Serving suggestions
Baked roots with smoked almond butter
　(pictured)
Tossed through fresh leaves with crunchy
　seeds and extra dressing
Served as part of a bowl with rice, ferments and
　cooked vegeables

The first trick is stripping the kale from the stems. Hold the stem at the bottom in one hand and then wrap your other hand around the first leaves at the base and pull that hand up the stem, cleanly taking off all of the leaves. Continue with the whole bunch. Keep the stems and very finely chop them, just discarding the woody end.

Drizzle your chosen oil over the kale leaves and finely chopped stems in a bowl and add the salt or tamari. Now rub the oil into the leaves (with energy) like you are giving someone a massage, kneading the leaves with the salt and oil. After a few minutes you will see the leaves start to soften, darken and eventually wilt, and will resemble cooked kale. You know they are ready when they start to 'squelch'. Depending on the season and the tenderness of the kale, this will take more or less time.

You can end here, but it would be a shame to miss out on the secret ingredient – the nut or seed butters. Add 1–2 tablespoons of your chosen butter and massage once more. Yes, it will get a bit messy, but it will be DELICIOUS!

Serve within a salad, in a sandwich, as a topping, or as part of a bowl. You can even bake this kale and turn it into crisps if you have some left over. Store in a sealed container in the fridge for up to five days.

FLAVOUR IDEAS

SUPER GREEN: Pumpkin seed oil, pumpkin seed butter, lemon salt and chilli (pepper) flakes
ULTIMATE ADDICTION: Toasted sesame oil, tahini and tamari
SATIATING: Olive oil, sunflower butter, hemp seeds, smoked sea salt

MILK CHOCOLATE MOUSSE

Making this recipe used to be our favourite lesson on the Plant Academy live courses, as it is such an effective way to showcase the huge variety of flavours in nut and seed milks. This mousse can be eaten like a chocolate pot or used as a dessert topping. You can replace the powders and add melted chocolate if you want it to set and also use it as a frosting Try this recipe with different nut and seed milks to discover your favourite combinations.

Serves: 2

Time taken: 40 minutes

1 avocado

100ml (3½fl oz/scant ½ cup) Plant Milk (page 38)

75ml (2½fl oz/5 tbsp) liquid sweetener, such as agave syrup or maple syrup

½ tsp vanilla extract

Pinch of ground cinnamon

Pinch of Himalayan pink salt

3 tbsp cacao powder

1 tbsp carob powder

Equipment

High-powered blender

Blend the avocado flesh, plant milk, liquid sweetener, vanilla extract, cinnamon and salt in a high-powered blender until thoroughly combined. Add the cacao and carob powder and blend again until smooth. Then chill for at least 30 minutes before tasting.

Store in a sealed container in the fridge for up to 4 days.

DIFFERENT NUT AND SEED MILKS YOU CAN USE

- Pistachio
- Brazil nut
- Walnut
- Pumpkin seed
- Hemp seed
- Pine nut
- Pecan

TIPS

- You can add 6 tablespoons of melted vegan dark chocolate (80% cocoa) instead of the cacao powder to create a set mousse.
- When experimenting with different nuts you can use, assess how much pulp was left behind on each try. Knowing how much pulp is produced can inform you which nuts are more commercially viable (produce less waste) and could even inspire new recipes that use the pulp.

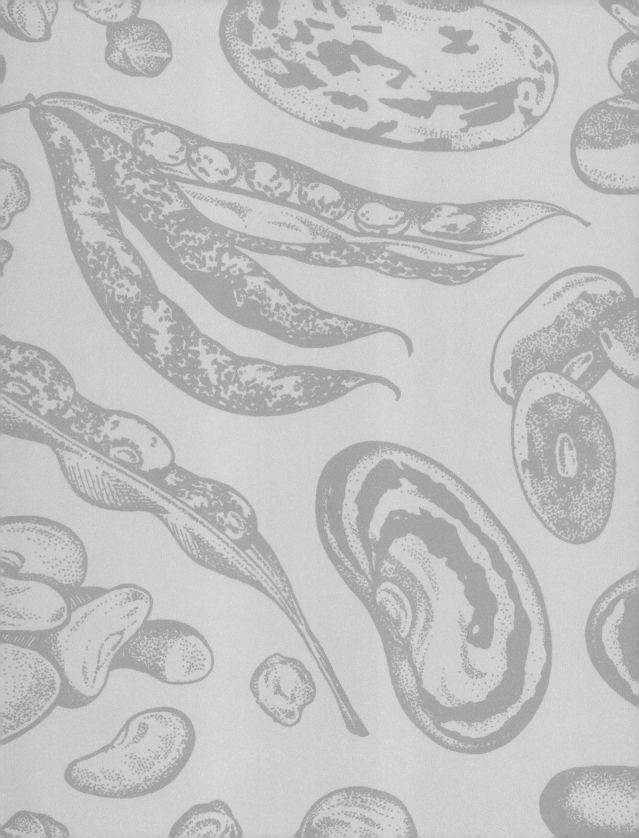

BEANS & LEGUMES

Beans have become globally recognized as a food for the future. During the UN's Global Innovation Hub at COP27 in Sharm el-Sheikh, Egypt, the SDG2 Hub officially launched the Beans is How coalition, with the aim of doubling bean consumption by 2028 and encouraging every restaurant to offer a bean dish so they are just as common as fish and meat options. The benefit of beans reaches far beyond their flavour, they also contain a huge amount of fibre and fix nitrogen in the soil for the planet.

Long gone are the days when beans were deemed boring. Now, in the UK, beans are bouncing off the shelves and brands such as Bold Bean Co. are rebranding beans and making them the hot new thing we all want to buy and cook with.

Beans are staples in many of our favourite foods such as hummus, tempeh and baked beans, and have been a culinary staple in cultures across the world for thousands of years, for example mung beans are used to make Indian breads, soy beans are to make Asian tofu and black beans for Mexican refried beans. Beans are easy to grow, and in England we can now find heritage UK-grown beans on shop shelves thanks to companies like Hodmedods, who are paving the way and bringing beans back home, and reconnecting chefs and foodies with native varieties – this is key to our future food revolution.

In the plant-based kitchen we have begun using aquafaba (tinned bean water) to make meringues, jumped on the sprout train thanks to Doug Evans (author of *The Sprout Book*), and started using beans in cakes. These powerful pulses give us excellent reason to take them seriously.

SPROUTING

Sprouting literally means to bring a seed to life. Sprouting, like fermentation, makes plants more easily digestible, makes their nutrition more bioavailable, and can be a great way to enjoy the simple pleasures of seeing something coming to life more and more each day. It's important to use organic seeds. You can sprout many kinds of seeds, beans and legumes, and there are three ways you can sprout them.

Harvest and enjoy!

TECHNIQUE 1

IN THE JAR

This method is best for broccoli sprouts, alfalfa sprouts, radish, sunflower, chickpea and mung bean.

Add 4 tablespoons of your chosen seeds to a 1 litre (34fl oz/1 quart) jar and add 200ml (7fl oz/scant 1 cup) of filtered water. Leave the seeds to soak at room temperature for at least 6 hours or overnight.

Rinse the seeds in a sieve then place them back into the jar, cover with a piece of cloth or a kitchen paper, and secure with a rubber band or string.

Find an ambient place to sprout your seeds – such as a shelf – that is out of direct light and not too warm.

Leave the jar on its side and repeat the process of rinsing the seeds morning and evening, each time returning them to the jar and re-covering it. Within a day or two the sprouts will start to grow. Alfalfa and radish are ready when the top blooms into a colourful shoot. For legumes, the tail of the sprout should not exceed the bean length. This will take 2–3 days.

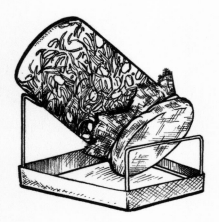

TIP – If you are sprouting chickpeas, they can be enjoyed in small amounts raw but are even better when lightly cooked. You can then make the most delicious sprouted chickpea hummus or use them in curries, soups and stir-fries.

KITCHEN PAPER METHOD

SOW THE SEEDS

For this method the best seeds to use are chia, camelina and cress.

Put a sheet of kitchen paper on a plate or tray. Get the towel wet (between just damp and soaking wet) and sprinkle on the seeds. You want an even coverage; the seeds can be close together but not overlapping.

Cover with another plate turned upside down in an ambient place (this keeps the atmosphere humid) and each morning and evening keep the towel moist by sprinkling it with water. After a few days you will see the sprouts start to grow.

Allow them to grow for 5–10 days until you have something green and a few centimetres/an inch or so high. At this point they are ready to harvest and enjoy.

This method of sprouting is best for pea shoots, buckwheat, broccoli sprouts and radish.

Start the same way as in the jar method on page 54, soaking and sprouting your chosen seeds for a few days.

When they sprout, fill a suitable waterproof container with 2.5cm (1 inch) of soil. Make sure you are using a container big enough for your seeds to spread out in.

Place the sprouted seeds on top of the soil and cover with another thin layer of soil.

Water everything and continue to keep this moist every morning and evening in an ambient place for a couple of weeks until the sprouts have grown.

COOKING

Using dried beans can be a cost-effective way to enjoy beans, and you can cook them in big batches and freeze them. Storing dried beans takes up less room than jars or cans of cooked beans if you are short on space and can be a nice way to control how your beans turn out.

When using dried beans, it is important to soak them (for the suggested soaking time), rinse them well and then cook them until al dente or completely soft, depending on what you intend to do with them.

Kombu seaweed can help make beans easier to digest. It does not affect the flavour or texture but can be used during the soaking process or when cooking, and after cooking can be finely chopped and folded through soups and stews or bean-ottos.

Another method used to cook beans is to add 1 teaspoon baking powder to the pot when cooking, but you must keep skimming off the foam from the cooking pot as they simmer.

BAKING, BINDING & THICKENING

Beans are used more than ever in sweet and savoury baking, as they add moisture and protein to all sorts of bakes. Think of black bean brownies, sweet potato bread and – more recently – sponges using white beans. With their soft texture and often quite subtle flavour beans are a great way to make nut-free treats.

In this chapter you will find a unique way of using beans in the desserts, this time in a cheesecake, where they can be used instead of nuts to create the body for a cream. You can also use beans as an ice cream base, in sauces, as a cream and anywhere where you're looking to get a thicker silky texture.

FERMENTING

In many cultures around the world, you will find beans used in fermentation; from soy beans and chickpeas in miso, soy beans in nato and tofu, to many different beans used in tempeh (see page 58) and the fermented chickpea flour batters in this book. Beans are a very versatile ferment and make a fantastic base for limitless plant-based dishes. With the benefit of being high in protein (and therefore satiating) they hold flavours, can be smooth or crispy, and are a natural centrepiece to any plate where you may otherwise see imitation meats.

TEMPEH

Traditionally made from cooked and fermented soy beans, tempeh is an amazing and versatile ingredient. To make it, you need to source tempeh starter culture, easily found online, which plays a crucial role in fermentation and holding the beans together to make a shape you can cut and cook. The following recipe uses British beans, but any bean or pulse can be used and the addition of grains works well too.

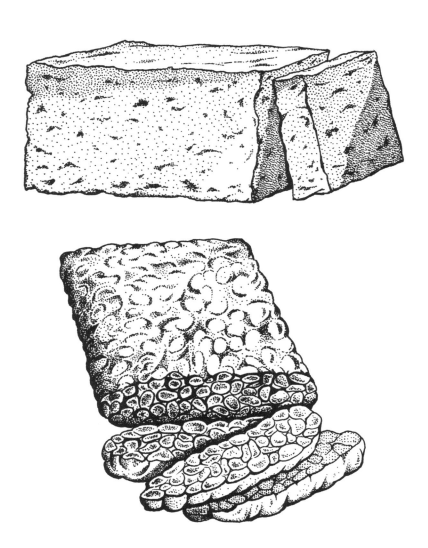

Serves: 4–5, makes 1 block of tempeh (about 300g (10½oz))

Time taken: 40 minutes, plus 8 hours soaking time and 3–4 days fermenting time

200g (7oz) dried beans, such as soy beans, chickpeas (garbanzo beans), mung beans or lentil beans

¼ tsp tempeh starter culture (Rhizopus spores)

1 tbsp apple cider vinegar

Equipment

Clean muslin (cheesecloth)

Biodegradable food bag or unsprayed banana leaves

Sterilized thick skewer

Dehydrator

TIP – Traditionally, the bean mix is wrapped in banana leaves, which allow it to breathe, but these days people often use food bags with plenty of air holes. These work brilliantly, but if you have access to unsprayed banana leaves, we recommend using them (securing them with toothpicks or kitchen string).

Soak the beans in a covered glass or non-reactive food-grade container with filtered water for 8–24 hours. If soaking for 24 hours, store in the fridge and change the water after 12 hours. Ensure your container is big enough and you use twice the amount of water of the beans as beans will expand.

Rinse the soaked beans very well then drain and put in a large pot. Cover with enough fresh filtered water to sit 7–8cm (2¾–3¼ inches) above the beans. Bring to the boil over a high heat, skimming away any scum that rises to the surface during cooking. Reduce the heat to low and simmer for 25–35 minutes or until the beans are tender but not quite fully cooked. You want the beans to be slightly undercooked as the final result requires the bean holds its shape.

Spread out and allow the beans to cool and dry on clean tea towels or the muslin (cheesecloth). This is vital, so that the correct mould grows. Let the mix cool to body temperature. Once cool and dry, peel the beans. Place the beans in a clean bowl with the vinegar and mix well. This step inoculates the beans and also ensures a good pH. Add the tempeh starter culture and mix evenly.

Put the mixture in a biodegradable food bag (perforated with holes about 1cm (½ inch) apart by a thick, sharp needle) and press to a thickness of 2cm (¾ inch). Seal the bag and press the mixture together as much as you can to form a compact, tight package. Place on a dehydrator tray at 30°C for 24–48 hours, depending on the humidity of your surroundings. (If you live in a more humid climate, tempeh will ferment without the dehydrator, just ensure it is still covered and safe from unwanted bacteria while fermenting.) Halfway through this time you will see the characteristic white robe of mycelium beginning to form. During fermentation, the mycelium forms an even coating that binds the beans together to form a solid block. Once the mycelium grows and the tempeh is formed, it is ready to enjoy. At this point, the tempeh should have a delightful mushroom-like aroma. Take the tempeh out of the dehydrator and allow it to cool completely before refrigerating or freezing.

Keep in the fridge for 3–4 days or seal in an airtight container and freeze for up to 3 months.

BEAN-OTTO

You will know by now that I am crazy about beans. This recipe shows you a different way to enjoy them, as a warming, elegant main dish. Bean-ottos are inspired by classic risottos. This dish looks like it's taken hard work to produce, but it actually requires little effort, and the best part of it all is that you are putting beans at the centre of the plate, surrounded by natural, minimally processed ingredients.

Serves: 2

Time taken: 45 minutes

For the kombucha-braised leek

2 tbsp olive oil

1 large leek, washed well and cut into 2.5cm
(1in)-thick rounds

100ml (3½fl oz/scant ½ cup) kombucha

2 tbsp Vegan Butter (page 148)

¼ tsp smoked sea salt

½ tsp cayenne pepper

For the bean-otto

3 tbsp olive oil

1 shallot, finely diced

1 small leek, white and green parts separated,
washed well and thinly sliced

1 garlic clove, finely minced

200ml (7fl oz/scant 1 cup) vegan white wine

1 x 400g (14oz) tin of butter (lima) beans,
drained – reserve the aquafaba (liquid from
the tin) – and rinsed

300g (10½oz) plain Cashew Cream (page 39)

Grated zest and juice of 1 lemon

½ tsp sea salt (optional)

½ tsp freshly cracked black pepper

¼ tsp dried chilli (pepper) flakes (optional)

To serve

Smoked Tofu Candy (page 85)

Leek oil

KOMBUCHA-BRAISED LEEK Heat the oil in a frying pan over a medium heat then add the leek, making sure the cut side of each piece is in contact with the pan. Cook for 5 minutes until golden then carefully turn each piece of leek to cook on the other side. Add the kombucha and let it sizzle away and the leeks cook through. Cook for 5 minutes, until the liquid has evaporated, then add the butter and cook for a further 5 minutes. The leek should be cooked through and golden on both sides. Finish with the smoked salt and cayenne pepper, turn off the heat and set to one side, ready to warm through before serving.

BEAN-OTTO Heat the oil in another frying pan over a low heat then add the shallot and a large pinch of salt and cook for 10 minutes until translucent. Add the green leek tops and garlic and cook for a further 5 minutes until everything is soft but not too coloured. Add the white wine in three large splashes, each time turning up the heat and deglazing the pan, making sure the liquid evaporates and you cook off the alcohol. Now add the beans, cashew cream and 200ml (7fl oz/scant 1 cup) of the aquafaba (if it contains salt, taste the bean-otto before seasoning with salt) and cook over a low heat for about 5 minutes until the sauce is thicker but still creamy and slightly runny with piping-hot beans. Add the lemon juice, salt (taste beforehand) and pepper and stir gently, being careful not to break up the beans.

Serve the bean-otto in bowls topped with warmed-through braised leek, a few pieces for smoked tofu candy, lemon zest, a good drizzle of leek oil and some dried chilli flakes (if you like).

TIPS

- As always, use whichever vegetables are in season: try a topping of smoked carrots and a paprika oil, or fresh asparagus, extra lemon and chilli oil, or grilled mushrooms and wild garlic oil.
- Try different beans: butter beans are fantastic due to their size, texture and flavour, but also try cannellini or black beans.

BEAN CHEESECAKE

Beans can make a fantastic base for creams, ice creams, cakes and candies. White beans especially are extremely versatile and carry all sorts of flavours really well. Beans are also low cost, quick to prepare and are more environmentally friendly. My wish is that, in the future, locally grown beans are our first port of call when creating sweet and savoury dishes and I hope this recipe inspires you to think differently about their potential.

Makes: 1 x 18cm (7in) round cake (8–12 slices)
or 5 x individual 10cm (4in) cakes
Time taken: 1 hour, plus 3 hours to set

For the spiced biscuit base
Biscuit Base (page 161) – use sunflower seeds
1 tsp ground cinnamon
¼ tsp nutmeg, grated

For the chocolate ganache
100g (3½oz) vegan dark chocolate (75–80% cocoa), finely chopped
120ml (4fl oz/½ cup) Plant Milk (page 38)

For the white bean mascarpone
1 x 400g (14oz) jarred butter beans, drained
300ml (10fl oz/1¼ cups) Plant Milk (page 38)
100ml (3½fl oz/scant 1/2 cup) honey, agave or maple syrup
75g (2½oz) light tahini
½ tsp sea salt
2 tsp vanilla extract or the seeds from 1 vanilla pod
100g (3½oz) cacao butter, melted
100g (3½oz) coconut oil, melted

Equipment
18cm (7in) round cake tin or 5 x 10cm (4in) cake tins
High-powered blender

SPICED BISCUIT BASE Follow the method on page 161, adding the spices and sunflower seeds. Press the base mix into your chosen tin, it should be about 1cm (½ inch) thick.

CHOCOLATE GANACHE Add the chopped chocolate to a medium-sized heatproof bowl. Bring the milk to boil in a small saucepan and then pour half over the chopped chocolate and begin to whisk, add the rest of the milk and continue whisking. You will see the chocolate melt and the mixture become glossy and smooth. Pour the mixture over the biscuit base and set in the fridge for 30–45 minutes, or freezer for 15–20 minutes, until set to touch.

WHITE BEAN MASCARPONE Put the beans, milk, chosen sweetener and tahini in a high-powered blender and blend until smooth. Then add the salt and vanilla. Stream in the melted cacao butter and coconut oil while the blender is running. Pour the mixture over the set ganache layer and set in the fridge for a further 2–3 hours. (I always prefer to set cheesecakes like this in the fridge as you can check they are ACTUALLY set and you get a much lighter texture than if you speed-chill them in the freezer. Once they have been frozen, they aren't quite the same.)

To serve, slice and plate up. Here I have kept it simple to let the beans speak for themselves but some fresh berries, a drizzle of caramel or some cool candied beans would be a great option.

The cake will keep in the fridge in a sealed container for up to 4 days and in the freezer for up to 1 month.

TIPS
– I love to include medicinal mushrooms in the biscuit base. Try adding 1 tbsp chaga tincture or powder to boost the flavour and feeling of this dessert. You can also try replacing the milk in the chocolate ganache to a chaga or reishi tea if you want to make this recipe completely nut and seed free.
– In this recipe I use jarred beans but you can explore also the possibilities of cooking your own beans.

CHICKPEA CHOCOLATE TRUFFLES

This low-sugar truffle recipe is perhaps a more surprising way to use beans, but chickpeas are a great base for rich chocolate recipes and are a wonderful alternative to usual nut-based truffles. They have a natural sweetness, as does the beetroot juice, and the earthy flavour of the beetroot pairs well with the other ingredients. Be careful to blend the mixture in stages so you get a smooth end result.

Makes: 20 truffles

Time taken: 30 minutes, plus 1 hour chilling

200ml (7fl oz/scant 1 cup) beetroot (beet) juice*

150ml (3½fl oz) Plant Milk (page 38)

250g (9oz) dark tahini

50g (1¾oz) maple syrup

400g (14oz) tinned chickpeas (garbanzo beans), drained and rinsed

10g (⅓oz) cacao powder

10g (⅓oz) carob powder, plus 20g (¾oz) extra for rolling

½ tsp sea salt

½ tsp ground cinnamon

¼ tsp cayenne pepper

300g (10½oz) vegan dark chocolate (80% cocoa), melted

Equipment

Food processor

*If you can't make or find beetroot juice, you can use any Plant Milk and increase the maple syrup by 30–40g (1–1½oz).

Put the beetroot juice, nut or seed milk and tahini in a food processor and process until thick and smooth, then add the maple syrup and chickpeas and process again until smooth, making sure all beans are very well combined. Add the cacao powder, carob powder, salt and spices and process again. Slow down the speed of the food processor and gradually drizzle in the melted chocolate: when it is mixed through, stop the food processor and pour the mixture into a container to set in the fridge for 1 hour.

When the mixture is set, put the extra carob powder in a bowl. Roll the truffle mix into about twenty 15g (½oz) balls then toss them in the carob powder.

The truffles will keep in an airtight container in the fridge for up to 5 days or in the freezer for up to 1 month. They will defrost pretty quickly or they can even be eaten partially frozen, giving the feeling of chocolate ice cream.

GRAINS & PSEUDO GRAINS

Grains and pseudo grains are the most common foods in the world. Whether it's white sushi rice in Japan, red rice in a delicious nasi campur (see page 88) in Indonesia, spice-infused long-grain rice in India, quinoa in sweet drinks and savoury stews in Peru, corn for soft and warm tortillas in Mexico, oats in your favourite morning porridge, or wheat making every bread you could imagine, they are, well, everywhere.

Grains and pseudo grains form as a satisfying starch at the centre of (or alongside) many meals, each one with a unique use in human cooking. How can we use them at their best, relishing the rich cultural recipes in which they feature, yet thinking consciously about including different types and not overusing the same varieties? Biodiversity is a Plant Academy priority, so think outside the box in the grains you choose, to optimize your creativity, gut health and the health of the planet.

Perhaps the most familiar grain is rice. It is a symbol of fertility and prosperity, forms part of ceremonies in Japan, and even has its own gods (for example in Japan, this god is called Inari). Pseudo grains (or pseudo cereals) such as quinoa, buckwheat, millet and amaranth, which are technically seeds, are also cultural staples and offer satiating substance to many meals. They can be turned into flours to be used in baking, or sprouted to make liquids such as rejuvelac for fermenting, buckwheat bread (see page 150) or puffed to add crunch to any dish.

In this chapter, we explore how to make the most of a biodiverse range of grains, learn how to cook different varieties and understand their role on our plates.

PREPARATION

To better understand the grains and pseudo grains in this chapter, it's useful to know how they can be prepared. As this book is gluten free, this list only includes gluten-free grains and pseudo grains. There are many more varieties, but the following are a good place to start. Note that all water used should be filtered.

COOK

All grains have different soaking and or cooking times. Here are some guidelines to make the most of each grain. Most will keep for up to 3 days after cooking if properly cooled (rinsed under water or spread onto a tray) and stored in a sealed container in the fridge.

Short-grain brown rice

This rice is nutrient dense and softer than its long-grain white relatives. Cook 1 part rice to 2 parts water in a covered saucepan over a medium heat for 35 minutes. I love to add seaweed (such as a strip of kombu) or a black or green tea bag when cooking brown rice to add flavour and boost nutrition. At the end of the cooking time, turn off the heat and place a piece of kitchen paper between the lid and saucepan to absorb the last of the water and end up with a fluffier rice. Brown rice can be served hot or used to make a wonderful cold salad with a herb vinaigrette, pesto or chilli oil stirred through the grains.

Brown basmati rice

A slightly quicker cooking brown rice. First wash the grains, then cook 1 part rice to 2 parts water for up to 20 minutes in a covered pan over a medium heat, using the kitchen paper method above at the end of the cooking time. You can enhance the flavour of this rice by adding spices when it cooks – try adding star anise or whole dried chillies to the cooking water – or sauté onions in plenty of oil with turmeric, garlic and chilli, stirring it through the rice when cooked.

Red rice

This rice is more flavoursome and nuttier than some other varieties. Soak in filtered water for up to 12 hours to speed up the cooking time and optimize nutrition. Rinse and cook 1 part rice to 2 parts water in a covered saucepan for 40 minutes, finishing with the kitchen paper method. Red rice is great with curries, tossed through spicy or aromatic salads and useful for any dish where you desire a more nutty and colourful grain.

Black rice

Black rice takes longer to cook than most varieties and you will often find it part-cooked and then cooked again with a stock or coconut milk. Soak in filtered water for up to 12 hours before cooking, to help speed up the cooking time and optimize nutrition. Rinse and cook 1 part rice to 3 parts water in a covered saucepan over a medium heat for 50–60 minutes (it can be made more delicious with the addition of seaweed such as kombu), then drain if needed. Serve, or cool the rice and warm through in a dark stock (see page 26) or sweetened milk such as coconut, which will turn into a dessert or even a breakfast porridge.

Wild rice

Technically not rice but a seed that looks a lot like black rice that needs cooking time of 1 hour with 1 part rice to 3 parts water in a covered saucepan over a medium heat, or bloom (see opposite). You will then need to drain the water from the rice as it absorbs less of the liquid and will remain al dente. Use wild rice in cold salads, mixed with other grains to boost texture and flavour, or bloomed in salads or rice paper rolls.

Quinoa (white, black, red)

Quinoa is best washed well before cooking. White quinoa cooks the quickest – in 10 minutes – while red and black take 12–15 minutes. Measure 2.5 parts water to 1 part quinoa, boil the water before adding the quinoa, then cover and cook it, finishing with the kitchen paper method for a fluffy end result.

Buckwheat

Buckwheat behaves quite uniquely as it becomes slightly gelatinous when cooked or soaked. Either cook 1 part buckwheat to 2 parts water in a covered saucepan over a medium heat for 15–20 minutes or soak in filtered water for 1 hour, then rinse and bake with 2–3 tbsp oil and 1 tsp spice such as fennel seeds or chillies in the oven, until crisp. Drain if needed and serve once cool. Buckwheat is nice served with stews and curries, in salads or with roasted vegetables.

Millet

This is totally underrated in the West yet a delicious ingredient that has a sweet and nutty taste. It can be lightly toasted in a pan before cooking to release its flavour, then cooked 1 part millet to 3 parts water in a covered saucepan over a medium heat, finishing with the kitchen paper method for 10–15 minutes.

Whole oat groats

We are familiar with rolled oats, but whole groats are wonderful. They can be used in place of rice in salads or risottos (see page 138 and have a sweet flavour and chewy texture. They are best soaked in filtered water and 1 tbsp of apple cider vinegar for 1 day before using, which helps to pre-digest them. Rinse and cook 1 part oats to 3 parts water or stock in a covered saucepan over a medium heat for 40 minutes. They can also be soaked, rinsed, dried completely in a dehydrator and then ground in a blender to make flour.

PUFF

Puffing grains is a great option to add texture to a dish – it can also be a way to use up excess cooked grains and can be done in bulk. To puff a grain, they first need to be cooked, following the guidelines above, then dried (ideally using a dehydrator). Once your chosen ingredient is dried, add enough of a neutral frying oil in a small pan so the oil is around 10cm (4 inches) deep (if making a small batch). Heat over a medium heat and test when the temperature is right by dropping just one grain inside to see if it puffs. If the oil isn't hot enough it will sink and if it's too hot it will burn.

Once the oil is the right temperature, fetch a spider or strainer spoon and line a tray with some kitchen paper. Carefully add the grains to the oil, see them quickly puff then scoop them out with the sieve and place on the paper, adding some seasoning such as sea salt, chilli or Tajin. Store in a sealed container in an ambient place for up to 1 week.

SPROUT

Sprouting is a wonderful way to amp up the nutritional benefits of different ingredients – you can read more about sprouting on page 54. In this chapter, sprouting is most relevant to quinoa and buckwheat. Sprouting involves soaking the grains in filtered water, rinsing and then keeping the soaked grains in a jar with a mesh sprouting lid and rinsing them every morning and evening for a few days until a tail forms.

BLOOM

Wild rice in particular is extremely nutritious and can even be eaten raw when prepared in this way. To bloom wild rice it first needs to be 'scored' in a food processor to lightly break it, then soaked in filtered water and put somewhere slightly warm. Change the water daily until you see the seed become curly, this will take 2–3 days. Rinse the sprouted grains, drain and flavour the wild rice as on page 68 or bake it, fry it or add it to stews for a great texture and nutty flavour.

BATTER

Grains can form a fantastic base for batters such as pancake batters, frying batters, uttapam or idli batters (made with rice). To make a batter using whole grains they need to be soaked for at least 12 hours in filtered water, rinsed, then blended with fresh water – you can choose how thick you want the batter to be.

Batters can also be made from grain flours such as oat, buckwheat and rice – each one will result in a different texture and flavours: rice-flour batter can be a great 'slurry' for coating and frying vegetables, oat-flour batter will be thicker and is great for sweet pancakes, and buckwheat has a more earthy flavour, ideal for galettes or injiri-style batters. See a guideline for the ratios on the chickpea pancake batter recipe on page 104.

SEASONAL POKE BOWL

This dish was inspired by the signature vegetable cereal dish of guest chef Jason Andrew Wood on our Plant Academy Level Two course. The star of the show here is a grain-based savoury granola, which is a fantastic way to add crunch to any dish. This recipe is a celebration of seasonal ingredients and can be adapted to any time of year or location. I hope it inspires your creativity. You can see this dish being plated on the cover of this book.

Serves: 2
Time taken: 30 minutes

For the savoury granola

1 tbsp olive oil
1 tbsp tamari
1 tbsp maple syrup
1 tsp dried chilli (pepper) flakes (optional)
1 tsp fennel seeds (optional)
1 tsp coriander seeds (optional)
100g (3½oz) gluten-free rolled oats
30g (1oz) sunflower seeds
30g (1oz) sprouted mung beans (optional)
30g (1oz) cooked quinoa or buckwheat
　(optional)

For the roots, fruits and shoots (choose as many as you like)

Thinly sliced root vegetables (here I used
　mandoline-sliced Candy Cane beetroot
　(beets))
Thinly sliced fennel
Thinly sliced courgette (zucchini) tossed in a
　little olive oil, lemon and sea salt
Tomatoes, cut into wedges
Radishes, but into halves and quarters
Fresh chillies, thinly sliced
Fresh sprouts
Fresh herbs, microgreens or edible flowers

Cultured Cashew Cream (page 33), to serve
Miso & Mustard Vinaigrette (page 32)

Preheat the oven to 180°C fan/200°C/400°F/gas 6 and line a large baking tray with baking paper.

SAVOURY GRANOLA In a large bowl whisk together the oil, tamari and maple syrup until combined then add the rest of the ingredients and mix everything together with a spoon, being sure the dry ingredients are thoroughly coated in the liquid. Set aside for 5 minutes.

Add the granola to the lined baking tray and spread it out so it is even and not too thick. Bake in the oven for about 30 minutes, shaking the mixture every 10 minutes. You want the granola to be cooked through and golden, not dark and not soft either.

Remove from the oven and leave the granola on the tray to cool. Once cool, store the savoury granola in a glass jar or sealed container outside of the fridge.

ROOTS, FRUITS AND SHOOTS Spend time preparing your vegetables while the granola bakes.

To serve, put a few tablespoons of the cashew cream in bowls, then add your chosen roots, fruits and shoots in sections around the bowl. Add the granola to one section and drizzle the entire bowl with dressing.

Once everything is mixed eat fresh! The bowl will not keep although you can keep granola in an airtight container for up to 1 month.

BUCKWHEAT FLATBREADS

This versatile three-ingredient flatbread recipe is a great way to introduce buckwheat flour into your diet. Buckwheat is a fantastic ingredient on its own and is also complementary to other flours but it can't be substituted 1:1 for other flours as it is more dense, with an earthy taste. Here, buckwheat is mixed with yoghurt to create a light dough that holds its shape and cooks quickly, to make an adaptable base for any savoury flavours.

Serves: 4

Time taken: 30 minutes

For the buckwheat flatbreads

400g (14oz/3 cups) buckwheat flour, plus extra
    for dusting
250g (9oz) plant-based yoghurt
½–1 tsp sea salt

FLAVOUR IDEAS

Marinated courgette (zucchini) ribbons, pesto
    and sun-dried tomatoes
Roasted squash, rocket (arugula), Cashew
    Cheese (page 113) and chilli oil
Massaged Kale (page 48), avocado and
    Smoked Salsa Macha (page 31)

FLATBREAD Put the flour, yoghurt and salt in a medium bowl and mix together to form a dough: start mixing using a spoon, then bring the dough together with your hands. Let the dough sit while you prepare the remaining elements.

Split the flatbread dough into four and dust a clean, dry surface with flour. Roll each flatbread out with a rolling pin to a 15–20cm (4–8 inch) diameter circle. Make sure there is enough flour, so that the flatbreads do not stick to the surface or rolling pin.

Heat a large frying pan over a medium heat then add a flatbread and cook for 2 minutes on each side, until cooked through and lightly toasted. Repeat with the remaining flatbreads.

Serve as a wonderful picnic spread, with each element ready to load onto the warm flatbreads. Add your chosen toppings and extra glugs of olive oil and sea salt.

TAMALES

Tamales are a Mexican street food made from corn masa (a flour made from corn). You make a corn dough, then fill it with flavours. My favourites include Venezuelan banana skin, beans, spicy squash, smoked tomatoes and this more British twist – hemp-seed pesto. The majority of corn is now genetically modified but in its native form it's a colourful and diverse crop. Seek out different varieties and try to choose non-GMO options.

Serves: 4

Time taken: 1 hour

For the seed pesto (page 34)

For the tamales

200ml (7fl oz/scant 1 cup) Light Stock (page 24)

200g (7oz/scant 1 cup) corn masa

1 tsp Himalayan pink salt

50ml (1½fl oz/3½ tbsp) olive or coconut oil

60ml (2fl oz/4 tbsp) harissa

8 large chard leaves or 8 large corn husks

For the corn relish

1 whole corn cob, kernels removed

3 tbsp olive oil

Large pinch of sea salt

½ tsp dried chilli (pepper) flakes

Squeeze of lemon juice

Equipment

Food processor

Steamer

SEED PESTO See page 34.

TAMALES Warm the stock through. Add the corn masa, salt and oil to the food processor and then gradually stream in the warm stock. Add the harissa and continue to process until you have a smooth dough. The dough should form a soft ball and should not crack when rolled out, but it should also not be too wet. When the dough is the right consistency, leave it to sit at room temperature for 10 minutes, wrapped in a bowl until ready to shape.

Lay a chard leaf or corn husk on a chopping board. Add about 100g (3½oz) of the dough. Flatten into a neat rectangle, around 4cm (1½ inch) wide and 1cm (½ inch) from the edge of the leaf or husk. The dough should be 5cm (2 inch) thick and when filled make sure there are no cracks and the filling is completely covered. Add about 1 tablespoon of hemp pesto along the bottom third of the tamale in a neat line. Fold the top of the tamale over the bottom, seal the edges and neaten the sides. Fold the leaf or husk around the edges. Continue to make all the rest of the mixture of dough, pesto and husks and leaves into tamales then place in a steamer over boiling filtered water. Steam over a medium heat for 20–30 minutes then allow to cool. The tamales will firm up once cool.

CORN RELISH Simply mix everything together and serve alongside tamales as a fresh salad.

To serve, present the tamales whole on a plate if using chard, or unwrapped if using corn husks. Enjoy with the corn relish on the side and extra hot sauce if you like a little heat!

LOST RICE BOWL

With Vegetable Treacle & Candied Carrots

Short grain black rice is nutritious and nutty and this 'Venus' variety is named after the goddess of love because Asian emperors considered it an aphrodisiac. Black rice can be prepared sweet or savoury like in this dish, as it holds and complements rich flavours. This recipe uses a dark stock (see page 26) to enrich the dish alongside smoky carrots and an acidic salad with creamy cashews to bring it all together.

Serves: 2-3
Time taken: 1 hour 30 minutes

For the vegetable treacle (see Glace on page 27)

1 litre (34fl oz/1 quart) Dark Stock (page 26)
75g (2½oz) dried chickpeas (garbanzo beans), soaked in filtered water overnight then rinsed

For the black rice

500ml (17fl oz) Dark Stock (page 26)
200g (7oz) black Venus rice, soaked overnight in filtered water then rinsed
1 strip of dried kombu

For the candied carrots

200g (7oz) carrots, julienned
3 tbsp olive oil
1 tsp smoked spicy paprika
1 tsp sweet paprika
½ tsp smoked sea salt

For the roasted cashew salad

50g (1¾oz) cashews
2 handfuls fresh salad leaves, washed and dried
3 tbsp olive oil
1 tbsp kombucha vinegar or vegan red wine vinegar
¼ tsp smoked sea salt

Preheat the oven to 180°C fan/200°C/400°F/gas 6.

VEGETABLE TREACLE See Glace on page 27.

BLACK RICE Bring the stock to the boil in a large saucepan without a lid, then add the rice with a strip of dried kombu. Cook for 30–40 minutes on a medium heat with the lid on or until the stock has been absorbed and the rice is wonderfully al dente. While the rice cooks, continue with the other elements.

CANDIED CARROTS In a bowl, toss the carrots with the oil and spices and the spread out on a baking tray lined with baking parchment and cook for 20 minutes, until soft and caramelized. Be sure to move them around the tray every 5 minutes.

ROASTED CASHEW SALAD Roast the cashews in the oven on a baking tray for 20–30 minutes until golden and deeply roasted, remove and leave to cool, then roughly chop. Add the fresh leaves to a bowl and toss them in the oil and vinegar, and add the smoked salt.

To serve, place 3 tablespoons of vegetable treacle in your bowl, add the black rice, then top with candied carrots, dressed salad and sprinkle over the cashews.

PLANTS

This chapter is all about the centrepiece of a dish, the ingredients that are being showcased and understanding main plates. It can be tempting when we're talking about main plates to think about protein and substitutions but the future of food I hope to see is plant focussed, without any over-processed, unnecessary ingredients, so this chapter is all about making vegetables the star.

Balancing plates made of plants involves giving them substance using sauces, oils and grains, and equal effort goes into each element rather than relying on a piece of meat or fish to do all the hard work. By using techniques that add bold flavours, such as smoking, marinating and cooking confit, humble vegetables can hold their own in any dish.

Over the last few years we have seen the rise in whole vegetable cooking. Chefs like Tom Hunt led the way in using whole plants in creative ways. David Bez championed 'big vegetable cooking' far beyond whole roasted cauliflowers. Other pioneering chefs include Richard Buckley, (see page 6) founder of Acorn and OAK restaurants, Kirk Haworth, who creates innovative vegetable menus at his restaurant Plates, and Derek Sarno, who brings mushrooms to new dimensions through his creative, flavour-packed food. Many of these people have appeared on our Plant Academy courses and I invite you to discover their restaurants, social media and books for more inspiration.

This chapter will teach you techniques to add fantastic flavours to plants and how you can make satiating large plates utilizing grains, beans, sauces, nuts and seeds alongside proper plant cooking.

SMOKING

If you have ever been to my workshops, you'll know I'm a little obsessed with smoking things. From smoked salads to smoked chocolate truffles there is just something so enticing about adding unexpected smokiness into a recipe.

COLD SMOKING

Cold smoking is commonly done with a smoking gun, a small gadget with a little engine and a compartment for burning wood chips, with a filter and a long tube that pumps the smoke into your chosen covered container. You can use different varieties of wood such as oak, hickory and maple, or/and use dried leaves and dried herbs to give food really interesting flavours.

When using a smoking gun, you need to put your prepared ingredients in a container, for example a bowl covered with eco wrap or a box with a small hole for the smoking gun 'pipe'. Insert the pipe and make sure that it is straight so the smoke can flow. You will need a lighter so when you turn on the machine and the air starts to move you can light the chips and start the smoking process. Smoke until the bowl is full of smoke then remove the pipe and immediately seal the hole where the pipe was. Leave the mixture to smoke until all the smoke dissipates. Taste and decide if you want to do another round: you can smoke ingredients multiple times. Something more dense like a chocolate truffle mix will most likely need more time smoking, but something like a dehydrated kale chip will only need two smoking rounds to absorb the flavour.

The benefit of using a smoking gun is that you don't need any other ingredients to create a flavour and because the whole process is cold you can smoke ingredients without changing their form. You're also giving them a smoky taste influenced by the wood or other things you used to smoke. They are reasonably inexpensive and portable pieces of kit that are extremely effective when used properly.

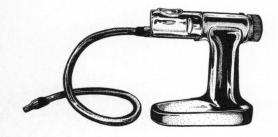

SMOKY SEAWEED CARROTS

One way you can create a smoked flavour is by cooking a plant with smoky ingredients, such as spices or oils, then use a smoking gun for optimum effect. This recipe transforms a carrot into a smoky, oily and wonderfully flavoursome component that can be used on pancakes, in salads or on toast.

Makes: 400ml (14fl oz/1¾ cups)

Time taken: 1 hour 30 minutes

2 sheets nori seaweed

4 large carrots, peeled, topped and tailed and halved lengthways

3 tbsp smoked sea salt

3 tbsp smoked paprika

400–500ml (14– 17fl oz/1¾–generous 2 cups) olive oil

Preheat the oven to 200°C fan/220°C/425°F/gas 7. Line a baking tin with a large sheet of foil and two sheets of baking paper (these layers will create a container so the oil can't escape). Place one nori sheet in the tin. Lay the carrot halves onto the nori sheet, squeezing them together as tightly as possible. Sprinkle the carrots with the smoked salt and smoked paprika then place the second nori sheet on top. Pour enough oil over the carrots and nori to completely submerge them – this is called cooking confit 'under oil'.

Seal the parcel with the paper and foil and cook in the oven for 1 hour until the carrots are perfectly soft, if you poke a sharp knife through a carrot it should be completely soft. Remove from the oven and allow to cool completely in the oil then pour the oil into a container to use for dressings. The nori here is especially tasty. You can tear it into smaller pieces and fold it through rice, for example.

Slice the carrots into 'lox'-style slices: place one carrot flat on a chopping board and very carefully, holding your knife horizontally in line with the carrot, slice the carrot into long, thin strips. Place the cut carrots in a large bowl, spread them out so there is as much surface area as possible, cover the bowl in eco wrap, then smoke with a smoking gun (oakwood or hickory wood chips work well) once or twice. Taste and, if ready, store in a sealed container covered with some of the smoky oil. These will keep in the fridge for up to 1 week.

TIP – Seaweed is an incredibly useful ingredient in plant-based cooking, not only for its assistance when cooking beans and grains, but also for increasing nutritional benefits and adding an unexpected flavour of the sea. In this recipe, nori seaweed infuses the oil and carrots to give a deeper salty and umami flavour that is a welcome addition. Remember with salts and sugars, layering is key for optimum taste.

HOT SMOKING

GRILLED MUSHROOMS

Hot smoking can be done in many different ways, but the way that is most accessible to the home cook or small restaurants is using a stove-top smoker, a metal box that sits on top of a stove. It usually has a shelf inside that you put just 1–2 teaspoons of wood chips underneath and then a layer of foil (to prevent ingredients touching the base and burning), then you add the ingredients and slide on the lid until it is almost closed but has a little gap. Turn on the heat (not too high) and watch – as soon as smoke starts to come out of the gap, close the box lid and continue to smoke for 3–5 minutes, then turn off the heat and leave the ingredients to continue to smoke in the container. You can peek inside, opening the lid a little to check on the depth of the smoking process but only open the lid when you think it is complete.

If you are smoking a large ingredient like a tomato you can repeat the process many times until it is fully cooked, or you can use something that's already partly cooked and finish it in the stove-top smoker.

This method will change the form of the ingredients by cooking them. It is best used for nuts, seeds, tomatoes, fruits, mushrooms and pre-cooked roots. It creates a lovely, deep barbecue-style taste.

This very simple marinated and grilled mushroom recipe is one that I return to time and time again. Mushrooms have a high water content and hold any marinade really well, so you often find them with oils, spices and herbs. White miso with its sweet and salty flavour is a great addition to any kind of mushroom cooking and here, to make a marinade, I mix it with water to make a paste, then add oil and a kick of chilli to create a really flavoursome, moreish and slightly caramelized end result

Makes: 250g (9oz) mushrooms
Time taken: 20 minutes

2 tbsp white miso
60ml (2fl oz/4 tbsp) filtered water
100ml (3½fl oz/scant ½ cup) olive or sesame oil

½ tsp dried chilli (pepper) flakes
250g (9oz) oyster mushrooms, cut into individual pieces or pulled into thin strips (sliced brown button mushrooms could also be used)

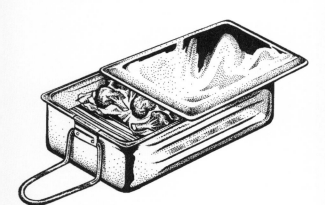

Whisk the miso, water, oil and chilli flakes together in a medium-sized bowl. Add the mushrooms and toss in the marinade.

Prepare the stove-top smoker with wood chips and place on the heat (not too high) and watch. As soon as smoke starts to come out of the gap, close the box lid and continue to smoke for 3–5 minutes, then turn off the heat and leave the ingredients to continue to smoke in the container. You can peek inside, opening the lid a little to check on the depth of the smoking process, but only open the lid when you think that it is complete.

Repeat 2–3 times until the mushrooms are cooked.

'MOLE' BLANCO

Nut sauces are a brilliant way of using stove-top smoker. In this method, to preserve the smoky flavour the nuts and seeds should not be soaked. This very non-traditional, simplified white mole features in the Adaptogen Adobo on page 91, and uses smoked pine nuts and cashews with spices and cacao butter to create a funky smoky sauce that can be used on many different plates.

Makes: 500ml (17fl oz/about 2 cups)
Time taken: 40 minutes

100g (3½oz) pine nuts
100g (3½oz) cashews
50ml (1½fl oz/3½ tbsp) olive oil
1 white onion, finely diced
1 tsp smoked sea salt
1 garlic clove, crushed
1 tsp Adobo dried chilli (pepper) flakes
100–180ml (3½–6fl oz/scant ½–¾ cup) cold
   filtered water (or cooled Light Stock,
   page 24)
¼ tsp cayenne pepper
30g (1oz) cacao butter, melted

Equipment
High-powered blender
Stove-top smoker

Set up the stove-top smoker with wood chips and foil, add the pine nuts and smoke on the heat for about 3 minutes, until lightly golden. Remove from the box and repeat with the cashews, smoking them on the heat for about 5 minutes before turning off the heat and leaving them to smoke a little more – again, they should be golden in colour and looking roasted.

Heat 2 tablespoons of the oil a frying pan over a low heat, then add the onion with a good pinch of smoked salt and cook for 10 minutes, stirring regularly, until translucent and just starting to caramelize. Add the garlic and chilli flakes and cook for 2 more minutes, then turn off the heat.

Add the pine nuts, cashews and cooked onion, garlic and chilli mixture to a blender with the water, the rest of the salt and cayenne pepper. Blend until totally smooth then stream in the remaining oil and the cacao butter. Taste for spice and seasoning then store in a sealed container in the fridge until ready to serve. It will keep for 5 days.

TIP – This nut sauce can be massaged into kale, served with Smoked Salsa Macha (see page 31) and avocado on toast, or even stirred through a risotto.

MARINADE

BBQ SAUCE

Marinating is a crucial part of many recipes and a great way to maximize flavour. Adding a raw ingredient to a marinade begins the softening and enhancing process that happens when cooking. Marinades usually consist of salty, acidic, sweet, oily and or enzyme-rich ingredients with the addition of herbs and spices. Think about a ceviche, for instance, where you add salt and acid to an ingredient to cold cook it (traditionally fish, but this also works for mushrooms), or when you add a rich marinade with ingredients such as tamari, coconut sugar and sesame oil to deepen the flavour of an ingredient such as tofu (see page 85).

When marinating, consider the density of an ingredient and the time it might require: the denser it is, the more time it will need. Also consider the water content of a plant – for example, marinating cabbage or cucumber in a salty sauce will release its water.

Marinades can be used for cold cooking but also high heat cooking. If you marinade a mushroom, for example, you will release some of the mushroom's water and amp up the flavour, then you cook it over high-heat or barbecue to intensify the flavours it has absorbed.

This is a very simple BBQ sauce that is tasty alongside many different vegetables and can also be used as a flavour enhancement when cooking.

Makes: 350g (12½ oz)
Time taken: 15 minutes

100ml (3½fl oz/scant ½ cup) infused oil (Spice Oil, page 31)
1 red onion, finely sliced
30g (1oz) root ginger, peeled and minced
3 garlic cloves, minced
2 fresh shiitake mushrooms, finely chopped
1 dried ancho chilli, rehydrated and seeds removed
1 dried chipotle chilli, rehydrated and seeds removed
50g (1¾oz) white miso
40g (1½oz) rapadura (whole cane) sugar
100ml (3½fl oz/scant ½ cup) filtered water

Heat the oil in a small frying pan on a medium heat and, once hot, add the onion, ginger, garlic and mushrooms and cook for 5 minutes until softened and starting to caramelize. Add the ancho and chipotle chilli and cook for a further 5 minutes and then add the miso and rapadura sugar, stirring well to combine. Turn off the heat and cool for a few minutes before adding to a blender with the water and blending until smooth. Store in a sealed container for up to 5 days.

SMOKED TOFU CANDY

This is a really tasty way to prepare tofu. Although I'm not a fan of making anything that imitates meat, this recipe almost ended up being named Tofu Bacon, before I thought better of it! Smoked tofu candy can be used in salads, as a flavourful texture to add to any savoury meal or even serve on soups or in sandwiches. You will find it in the Bean-otto recipe on page 60.

Serves: 2–3

Time taken: 1 hour

2 tbsp tamari

3 tbsp maple syrup

3 tbsp olive oil

1 tsp smoked hot paprika

1 tsp sweet paprika

½ tsp smoked sea salt

1 piece of firm tofu (250g/9oz), cut into thin strips

Mix the tamari, maple syrup, olive oil, smoked paprika, sweet paprika and salt in a medium bowl. Add the tofu strips to the bowl and lightly toss them in the marinade so they are well covered. Leave to marinate for 30 minutes.

After 30 minutes, preheat the oven to 160°C fan/ 180°C/350°F/ gas 4 and line a large, flat baking tray with baking paper.

Put the tofu and marinade on the baking tray and spread out the tofu so each piece is flat. Bake in the oven for 20 minutes, then turn each piece over and bake for a further 10 minutes or until the tofu is caramelized and firm. Remove from the oven and leave to cool completely.

Store the smoked tofu candy in a sealed container in the fridge for up to 5 days.

NASI CAMPUR

This classic Balinese dish is one of my ultimate favourites, the rice surrounded by tasty greens, tempeh and salsas. Traditionally this dish contains meat, but you find plant-based versions all over Bali. It is a great example of a dish where each element shines on its own but together form a satisfying plant-based main meal. The beauty is that in all its variations, the flavours work together to create something really enjoyable to eat.

Serves: 4

Time taken: 1 hour

For the sambal matah

2 makrut lime leaves

5 shallots, finely sliced

1 lemongrass stalks, finely sliced

1 red chilli, deseeded and finely sliced

1 tsp sea salt

3 tbsp coconut oil

For the tempeh manis

60ml (2fl oz/4 tbsp) coconut oil

1 red onion, finely diced

1 red pepper, cut into long, thin strips

½ tsp sea salt

200g (7oz) tempeh, cut into 1cm (½in) cubes

1 red chilli, deseeded and thinly sliced

1 tsp sweet paprika

For the sesame basil

Bunch of basil (about 15g/½oz)

2 tbsp light tahini

1 tbsp filtered water

1 tsp tamari

1 tbsp coconut oil

½ tsp cayenne pepper

For the coconut greens

1 tbsp coconut oil

1 tbsp Sambal Matah (see above)

100g (3½oz) leafy greens, kale or spinach

1 tsp tamari

400g (14 oz) (uncooked) Red Rice (page 68), 40g (1½oz) Candied Peanuts (page 40) and 200g (7oz) Grilled Mushrooms (page 82), to serve

SAMBAL MATAH Soak the lime leaves in a little warm water for 2–3 minutes to refresh them. Add the shallots, lemongrass and chilli to a bowl and lightly massage to soften. Drain the lime leaves, chop finely and add them to the bowl with the coconut oil and salt. Mix well and set aside.

TEMPEH MANIS Heat 2 tablespoons of the coconut oil in a large frying pan over a medium heat, add the onion, pepper and salt. Cook for about 10 minutes, until both are cooked through and lightly caramelized, then add the tempeh with the remaining 2 tablespoons of coconut oil and continue to cook for about 10 minutes until the tempeh is golden on all sides. Add the sweet paprika and chilli and cook for a further 2 minutes, then set aside until serving.

SESAME BASIL Preheat the oven to 180°C fan/200°C/400°F/ gas 6 and line a large baking tray with baking paper.

Pick the leaves from the basil stems and set aside. Mix the rest of the ingredients together in a small bowl to form a smooth paste. Dip the leaves in the sesame sauce one by one and lay them on the tray, then bake in the oven for 30 minutes, until crisp, turning them halfway through. The idea is they look fried without being fried, and add a slightly creamy, crispy element to the dish. Store leftover leaves in a sealed container in the fridge and enjoy as a snack!

COCONUT GREENS In Bali they cook the most delicious greens I have ever tried, using wonderful leaves like papaya and banana blossom. This is a much-simplified version of what they do. Simply heat the coconut oil in a frying pan over a medium heat, add the tablespoon of sambal matah, then the leaves, and let them cook down for 2 minutes, finishing with a splash of tamari.

To serve, put the rice in the middle of the plate and surround it with the other ingredients. I like to respect the more traditional plating style here – it also makes it fun to eat as you try all of the different flavours.

ADAPTOGEN ADOBO

With Mushroom Mole

This dish takes inspiration from the flavours of Mexico with Mole blanco and a rich mushroom Adobo, marinaded mushrooms and greens. With the flavoursome dark mole sauce we build flavour, topped with the mole blanco to cut through the richness of the dish. The mushrooms and greens then give body to the plate.

Serves: 4

Time taken: 2 hours

For the Adobo sauce

1 dried guajillo chilli

2 dried ancho chillies

Splash of olive oil

¼ tsp smoked sea salt

1 white onion, finely diced

2 plum tomatoes, finely chopped

3 garlic cloves, crushed

½ tsp ground cumin

1 tbsp lion's mane mushroom powder

40g (1½oz) cacao butter

2–3 tbsp mushroom 'treacle'

For the wilted kale and mushrooms

2 kale stems, washed

60ml (2fl oz/4 tbsp) olive oil

150g (5½oz) mix of shiitake or oyster
    mushrooms, cut into even pieces

Pinch of sea salt

1 garlic clove, crushed

For the potato bread

100g (3½oz) floury potatoes (e.g. King
    Edwards), washed and cut into quarters

100g (3½oz) gluten-free flour (quinoa,
    buckwheat or a gluten-free mix will work
    well), plus extra for dusting

1 tsp dried oregano

To serve

1 batch of 'Mole' Blanco (page 83)

Microgreens, such as nasturtium

½ tsp smoked sea salt

Equipment

Non-sealed blender (where the air can
escape). If you are using a Nutribullet or
similar make sure the sauce is completely
cooled before blending.

ADOBO SAUCE Preheat the oven to 180°C fan/200°C/400°F/gas 6. Place in the three dried chillies (on a tray or wire wrack) for 10 minutes. Transfer to a heatproof bowl and pour boiling water (just enough to fully cover) over them to rehydrate for 5 minutes.

Heat a splash of olive oil in a large saucepan over a medium heat, add the smoked salt and the onion and cook for 10 minutes until softened and starting to colour. Add the chopped tomatoes and cook for 5 minutes until the tomatoes have broken down slightly. Add the garlic and cook for a minute, then add the cumin and cook for a further minute. Roughly chop the hydrated chillies and take out the seeds, then add them to the pan with the with 200ml (7fl oz/scant 1 cup) of the reserved mushroom stock and simmer for 10 minutes. Turn off the heat and leave to cool for 10 minutes.

Blend the sauce with the lion's mane powder and cacao butter until silky smooth, then add 2–3 tablespoons of the mushroom treacle to round off the flavour. Set aside.

WILTED KALE AND MUSHROOMS Strip the kale leaves from the stems and finely chop the stems. Heat the oil in a large frying pan over a medium–high heat, add the mushrooms and a pinch of salt. Fry for about 3 minutes until golden, then near the end of the cooking time, add the kale stems with the garlic and cook for 1 minute before adding the kale leaves to wilt.

POTATO FLATBREAD Bring a medium pot of filtered water to the boil and add the potatoes to cook for 10 minutes, or until soft. Drain the water and add the potatoes to a food processor (they can also be mashed for a less smooth result). Process until smooth – it is important this happens when they are still hot – then add the flour and seasonings until you have a smooth and well-formed dough that rolls easily into a ball. If it does not and is too soft, add more flour 1 tbsp at a time.

Split the dough into 4 pieces and roll it out on a floured surface into a 3mm (⅛ inch) thick oval. Heat a frying pan (without oil) and place the flatbreads in it one at a time, cooking each for 2 minutes on each side until lightly golden and clearly cooked. Keep the bread in the pan until ready to serve, but make sure everything else is nearly ready!

To serve, heat the Adobo sauce in a small saucepan until warm, then place a ladleful (about 150ml/5fl oz/⅔ cup) on each plate. Add the mole blanco to the middle of the sauce in a circle. Top with the mushrooms and kale. Finish with the nasturtium leaves, smoked salt and the potato bread at the side of the plate.

SMOKED BROCCOLI AREPA

Arepa are a traditional South American dish made of corn and enjoyed like a sandwich. These arepa use a simple, delicious corn dough, cooked and loaded with flavourful 'pulled' broccoli stems, smoked broccoli florets and pickled broccoli, to use all parts of the broccoli. There are quite a few elements here, but you can enjoy each element on its own, for example using the kale in a sandwich, the tahini on top of a soup or the broccoli in a stir-fry.

Serves: 4

Time taken: 45 minutes

For the broccoli 'gherkins'

100ml (3½fl oz/scant ½ cup) filtered water

2½ tbsp apple cider vinegar

1 tsp organic cane sugar

1 tsp sea salt

2.5cm (1in) piece of broccoli stem, thinly sliced, with base trimmed and woody edges peeled

For the smoked broccoli

1 head of broccoli (200g/7oz), in small florets

1 tsp sea salt

1–2 tbsp olive or sesame oil

For the barbecued broccoli stem

1–2 tbsp olive oil

1 broccoli stem (about 150g/5½oz), peeled and thinly sliced into long strips (julienne)

Pinch of sea salt

75ml (2½fl oz/5 tbsp) BBQ Sauce (page 84)

For the arepa

150g (5½oz/generous 1 cup) Harina PAN (pre-cooked corn) flour

300ml (10fl oz/1¼ cups) warm filtered water

½ tsp chilli powder

½ tsp sea salt (or smoked sea salt for extra flavour)

Neutral oil, for frying, such as grapeseed

To serve

Smoked Salsa Macha (page 31), microgreens, avocado

Tahini Sauce (page 33), optional

Equipment

Stove-top cooker or smoking gun

BROCCOLI 'GHERKINS' Warm the water, vinegar, sugar and salt in a saucepan until simmering, then pour the mixture over the sliced broccoli stem in a heatproof bowl or jar. Leave to cool and pickle for 1 hour then store in the fridge for up to 5 days.

SMOKED BROCCOLI Cut the broccoli head into small florets, toss with the salt and oil and leave to sit for a few minutes.

BARBECUED BROCCOLI STEM Heat the olive oil in a large frying pan over a medium–low heat, then add the broccoli stem strips and a pinch of salt. You will see them start to soften. Add a splash of filtered water and cook for about 5 minutes, then add the BBQ sauce and cook for 10 minutes on a medium heat until you have a sticky and soft 'pulled' broccoli.

SMOKED BROCCOLI Place the florets in a stove-top smoker with wood chips and foil and smoke until the broccoli is cooked through and smoky. Alternatively, use a smoking gun: heat a frying pan over a medium–high heat with the oil and cook the broccoli until lightly charred. Place in a bowl, cover with eco plastic wrap and smoke with a smoking gun (see page 80).

AREPA Put the flour in a bowl, pour over the water, add the chilli powder and salt and mix to form a dough. Leave to sit for 10 minutes. Then take about 50g (1¾oz) of the dough and make it into a flat patty about the diameter of a coaster and 1.5cm (¾ inch) thick. Repeat 8–10 times. The trick here is to use the palm of your hand to get a smooth shape. The dough should be easy to work with – if it is too wet add flour, if it's too dry add water.

Preheat the oven to 160°C fan/180°C/350°F/gas 4. Heat a splash of oil in a frying pan over a medium heat then add the arepa and cook for 3 minutes on each side, until golden. Transfer to a baking tray lined with baking paper and place the arepas in the oven for 20 minutes until puffed up and cooked through. Remove from the oven and one by one hold them in a tea towel so you don't burn your hand, cut them though the middle (like a burger bun) and load with the sauces and different broccolis.

THE WORLD OF FERMENTATION

THE ART OF FERMENTATION

By Rachel de Thample

Award-winning author and chef

Fermentation is a transformative alchemy where raw ingredients are preserved in a manner that not only extends their shelf life, but also increases nutrients and metamorphosizes flavour. Arguably, it's the healthiest way to preserve food and, in my mind, the most exciting. Most ferments are also incredibly simple.

Sauerkraut, for instance, starts with just two ingredients: cabbage and salt. Packed into a jar, the vitamin C content increases (by up to 50%) and beneficial bacteria naturally living on the veg multiply. This can give your microbiome a healthy boost and enable us to assimilate the nutrients in our food more easily. It also dramatically enriches texture and taste. As the bacteria convert the natural sugars and starches in the veg into lactic acid, it creates a delicious tongue-tingly tang with addictive powers. Further cause for celebration is that fermentation makes food safer, as the magical acidification it creates destroys pathogenic bacteria.

Once you know the correct ratios and right environment, the plant kingdom is your oyster. You can use the most basic recipe as a canvas and the changing seasons' palette of colour as your paint. Swap red cabbage or beetroot for white cabbage to create a red kraut, or add carrot and turmeric for a golden glow. Delve into the world of herbs and spices for further flavour accents, as well as a probiotic boost, since these additions quell bacteria in your gut.

The multi-sensory and artful science of fermentation engages you on every level. Massaging salt into veg can be incredibly therapeutic, and consuming homemade ferments can be likened to the benefits of eating local honey. You're connecting to your environment through food. Once you have your ferment bundled into a jar, you can experience the wonderful sights and sounds of it bubbling away. When you ferment tea with sugar, you can witness the magic of emerging bacteria. Whilst the smell of fermented foods might prove divisive, the umami-rich dance offered to the palate is rewarding compensation.

Fermenting food fosters culture in every sense. It awakens primitive instincts, allowing us to connect with the world in a deeper way. It also reunites us with ancient roots; my granny made sauerkraut which led me to her German ancestry. Equally, fermented foods help us to survive. Each spoonful of fermented food has billions of bacteria that help to replenish and diversify the populations in our gut, which are constantly under attack.

I love Lauren's guide to fermentation. She starts with the basics to give you grounding and confidence. Then (what I find most exciting!), she introduces you to enticing recipes that allow fermented foods to shine and stand on their own as creative, nutritionally dense dishes. If you're not already addicted to fermented foods, this chapter will have you hooked.

THE BASICS

The word fermentation comes from the Latin 'fervere', which means to bubble or to boil. Technically, fermentation is a form of cold cooking. For those of you who enjoy any sort of laboratory-style cooking, fermentation may just hit the spot. These techniques are ancient practices that when adapted with modern ideas can transform the flavour of a dish. As cooks and chefs, we have the chance to share these benefits of flavour, gut health and ancient wisdom through the plate. There are books with fermented recipes, but this book takes this a step further so you're actually using them as an ingredient in your kitchen.

These pages provide fermentation techniques which you can then put to use in the base recipes that follow, and in dishes throughout this book.

LACTO FERMENTATION

Lacto fermentation is responsible for some of our favourite and most familiar ferments, including pickles, krauts, kimchi, butter, yoghurt and cheese. They also play a role in the production of beer, whisky, miso and soy sauce.

In these fermented products we create a colony of naturally-occurring bacteria on the vegetables or dairy products and cultivate that colony by creating an environment they like. Lactic acid bacteria eat sugars and produce lactic acid as a by-product, which generally makes these types of ferments more sour over time. These ferments are anaerobic ferments which means you are fermenting them in a closed airtight jar and allowing the process to happen.

SCOBY

'Symbiotic culture of bacteria and yeast' is the culture from kombucha, which is a fermented liquid most commonly consisting of caffeinated tea and sugar. A SCOBY looks like a cloudy mat that sits at the top of the ferment and its function is for the yeasts to consume the sugar to produce alcohol and then the bacteria – acetic acid bacteria – consume the alcohol to produce acetic acid which means that the result of fermentation is a slightly acidic and lightly alcoholic liquid.

Kombucha is an aerobic ferment which means we are working with the bacteria in our natural environment and cultivating the probiotic benefits. It is a great ingredient to use for fermenting other things. You will see I tend to ferment cheesecakes and creams with this particular culture.

Kombucha can also be used as a base for salad dressings and even for cooking, like in the braised leeks on page 60.

Once you master the basics of this wonderfully wild ferment, you have endless possibilities to make caffeine-free kombuchas, coffee kombuchas or even crazy flavours like popcorn or pine tree. See the recipe on page 105 to get started.

WILD FERMENTATION

PRESERVING WITH SALT

Wild fermentation relies on the microbes all around us to inoculate out ferments. These ferments include sourdough, ginger or turmeric bugs, tepache and even natural wine.

These ferments are generally more funky and less predictable than some other ferments, so you can support their process by using a starter culture, which involves inoculating the mixture with an existing culture of known microbes. So, like in sourdough bread, you will use the mother to inoculate the next batch of bread. In these ferments, we also work with the bacteria naturally occurring on the ingredients we are using, like in tapache and ginger bugs. The ingredients are the ginger or pineapple, sugar and water. We are working with the bacteria in the environment for some of the fermentation time, and without the air for the rest of the time.

Although this isn't technically a form of fermentation, it is a form of preserving ingredients so I wanted to include it as it is a very useful practice in the kitchen. This technique often involves citrus like lemons, oranges, limes and grapefruits, lots of salt and sometimes spices. It is great for preserving excess citrus peels that otherwise go to waste, and over time you have some interestingly flavoured ingredients to work with. Preserved Orange Hummus (see page 109), preserved grapefruit vinaigrette, and preserved lime and vegan white chocolate are some of my favourites.

LESSON

Before starting any form of fermentation, the most important thing to understand is that you are working with bacteria, trying to cultivate 'good' bacteria in order to create a delicious end result. The jars you are using must be sterilized, hands must be clean (or wear gloves), and the area in which you are working must also be clean: if any 'bad' bacteria get into the mix you are likely going to end up with something inedible.

When making ferments remember that fermentation takes place mostly outside of the fridge, I always suggest finding a spot in your kitchen where you would be happy to sit for a long period of time, somewhere not too hot or cold, not too near the oven or a source of different smells, somewhere where there is some airflow and light (but not too much).

SAUERKRAUT

Sauerkraut is a pretty straightforward lacto-ferment: the key ingredients are simply cabbage and salt. You can add a wider range of vegetables, like carrots or fennel, and spices, such as garlic and caraway or star anise and clove. This base recipe allows a lot of room to get creative, and I have added flavour ideas for you to explore as you master this process.

Makes: 500ml (17fl oz/generous 2 cups) jar
Time taken: 20 minutes, plus 4–10 days fermenting time

1 medium white cabbage
2–3 tbsp sea salt

FLAVOUR IDEAS

Golden Kraut

1 tbsp brown mustard seeds
½ tbsp yellow mustard seeds
½ tbsp ground turmeric
20g (¾oz) turmeric root
1 carrot, peeled into ribbons

Red Kraut

1 red cabbage
2–3 tbsp smoked sea salt
1 beetroot (beet), peeled into ribbons
3–4 star anise
A few cloves (for a festive feeling)

Pink Kraut

½ red cabbage
½ white cabbage
2.5cm (1in) ginger, sliced
1 garlic clove , peeled
1 fresh red chilli, finely sliced (adjusted to your preferred heat)

Equipment

2 x 500ml (17fl oz) or 1 x 1 litre (34fl oz/1 quart) jar, sterilized

TIP – This recipe will keep for at least 3 months in the fridge.

Carefully cut the cabbage in half. Discard the wilted, limp outer leaves, then keep a few of the fresher outer leaves to use later. Quarter the cabbage and trim out the core, also keeping it for later. Slice each quarter down its length, making 8 wedges. Slice each wedge crosswise into very thin ribbons.

Transfer the cabbage to a large mixing bowl and sprinkle the salt over the top. Toss the salt through the chopped leaves and leave it to sit for 5–10 minutes, then begin to work the salt into the cabbage by massaging and squeezing with your hands. At first, it might not seem like enough salt, but gradually – after 5–10 minutes – the cabbage will become watery and soft, looking almost like it is cooked. Once there is at least 250ml (8¾ fl oz/ 1 cup) of liquid in the bowl, add any spices or extra vegetables.

Transfer handfuls of the cabbage into your sterilized jars and firmly press down into the jar to compact them and release more juice. Make sure there are no air bubbles; work in layers, pressing down each one as you go. Repeat this until you've almost filled the jar, leaving a space for expansion (at least 5cm/ (2 inches) from the top of the rim of the jar). Pour the remaining brine over the cabbage, making sure it is covered with at least 3cm (1 inch) of brine. To keep the cabbage under the brine you can use the leaves and stem you reserved earlier to place over the top of the cabbage (they must also be submerged in liquid or it will go mouldy) or you can use a ceramic fermenting weight. Close the lid, put the jar on a plate to catch any liquid that may come out over the next few days and leave to sit somewhere out of direct sunlight and at room temperature for 4–10 days.

Check your sauerkraut daily and press it down (with clean hands) if the cabbage is floating above the liquid. Be aware that fermentation produces carbon dioxide, so the pressure will build up in the jar and needs to be released daily, especially in the first few days when fermentation will be most vigorous.

When the fermentation process is complete, open the jar and remove the weights, then chill in the fridge.

SAUERKRAUT FRITTERS

& Cultured Cream

Sauerkraut can be enjoyed for its benefits in salads, sandwiches, or as part of a main meal. This recipe is less for the probiotic benefits of the fermentation and more for the pure joy and flavour! See page 103 for an image of this recipe.

Makes: 10–15 fritters

Time taken: 30 minutes plus overnight fermenting

For the cultured chickpea batter

200g (7oz) chickpea (gram) flour

1 tsp smoked sea salt

¼ cayenne pepper

300ml (10fl oz/1¼ cups) filtered water

For the sauerkraut fritters

200g (7oz) drained sauerkraut (any flavour) (page 102)

200g (7oz) Cultured Chickpea Batter (see above)

Sunflower or grapeseed oil, for frying

Cultured Sour Cream (page 113) made with sauerkraut brine, to serve

Equipment

High-powered blender

TIP

– This chickpea batter is also great to make pancakes, and you can use many different flavours. For example you could add:

2 tsp ground nori as it is mineral rich and salty

1 tbsp charcoal and 1 tsp miso for black pancakes

1 tsp ground turmeric, 1 tsp sea salt and 1 tsp freshly ground black pepper for a golden variety

CULTURED CHICKPEA BATTER Blend the flour, smoked salt and cayenne pepper with filtered water and transfer to a glass jar and leave covered on the side in an ambient place overnight.

The next morning check that there is a light bubble in your batter. If so, it's ready to use.

SAUERKRAUT FRITTERS Drain the saurkraut from the brine (you can reserve this brine for dressings) and lightly press to remove any excess liquid. Mix the sauerkraut, the chickpea batter and in a medium mixing bowl so that the kraut is well coated in batter.

Heat a 10cm (4 inch) depth of oil in a small saucepan – it should be half full – over a medium heat until the oil is about 180°C/400°F. You can drop a tiny piece of batter into the oil to check it's hot enough; it should sizzle.

Line a baking tray with kitchen paper ready for the fritters after cooking, this will absorb excess oil.

Using a tablespoon, carefully place some of the battered sauerkraut mixture in the oil and cook for 1–2 minutes until golden then, with a slotted spoon, turn the fritter over to cook the other side for another 1–2 minutes. Once golden, use a slotted spoon to transfer the fritter from the oil to the lined baking tray, then repeat with as many fritters as you want to make. The uncooked mixture will be keep for 2 days in the fridge.

Serve the hot fritters with cultured sour cream.

KOMBUCHA

The process of making kombucha can feel quite mystical, but it is actually very simple. Once you have developed a strong and active ferment with this base recipe you can experiment with it. You can use different teas (as long as they don't contain oil) and sugars, and make interesting syrups and infusions for the second stage of fermentation. You can also explore endless possibilities with the fermented liquid and the SCOBY itself.

Makes: 1l (34fl oz/4–5 cups) kombucha
Time taken: 1 week

4 black tea bags or 2 tbsp black loose-leaf tea
150g (5½oz) organic cane sugar
200ml (7fl oz/scant 1 cup) starter liquid
1 whole SCOBY

Equipment

2-litre (68fl oz/2 quarts) sterilized glass container
Clean muslin (cheesecloth)
Rubber band or string

TIPS

– If you ever want to pause this cycle you can happily leave the brew with plenty of liquid without topping up for some time and the SCOBY will just keep growing. Never put it in the fridge or you will kill the bacteria. After some time, you can take some of this liquid and start again, but this liquid is best used as vinegar as it will be very sour.
– The only things that can go wrong with this fermet is if it dries out, or bugs or bad bacteria get inside. Both can be followed by following the best practice guidelines here.
– If your brew over-fermets (becomes too acidic to drink) it will have become an incredible vinegar for dressings and cooking.

Place the tea bags and sugar in a heatproof jug or bowl and pour over enough boiling filtered water to dissolve the sugar (about 300ml/10fl oz/1¼ cups). Let the tea steep for 20 minutes and stir to completely dissolve the sugar, then take out the tea bag or strain the loose-leaf tea and top the brewed sweet tea with 500ml (17fl oz/generous 2 cups) room-temperature filtered water. The whole brew should now be room temperature.

Add this brew to the glass container and add another 500ml (17fl oz/generous 2 cups) room-temperature filtered water, the starter liquid and the SCOBY. Cover with a towel and secure using an elastic band or string around the neck of the jar to keep a tight seal (to prevent fruit flies from contaminating the kombucha).

Leave the kombucha at room temperature, in an environment with a consistent temperature, to ferment for at least 7–10 days the very first time. For a sweeter kombucha, stop the fermentation process after 5 days. For a less sweet, more intense kombucha flavour, allow it to ferment for up to 15 days. Taste a little of the brew every so often and when you like the taste, pour all but 200ml (7fl oz/scant 1 cup) of the liquid into a clean swing-top bottle.

Now you can add more flavour – this is called second-stage fermentation. Some suggestions: goji berry and fresh ginger, fresh and dried raspberries, butterfly pea and lemongrass. When adding flavours at this stage, go for 1–2 tablespoons per bottle. If you add sweeter ingredients you will make a more carbonated drink. At this stage it is important to open the lid every day to let out the air (so it doesn't explode!). Taste it daily for 1–3 days and, when you like it, store it in the fridge: this will dramatically slow down the fermentation process but the liquid will continue to evolve over time.

The 200ml (7fl oz/scant 1 cup) of liquid and SCOBY you have kept can then be topped up with fresh tea and sugar, following the process above to start again.

KOMBUCHA-LITAS

Kombucha is one of the most fabulous ferments to use in drinks. It works well as a mixer and a strong base for an alcohol-free concoction. This recipe is inspired by the Mezcalitas of Mexico, and you can alter the fruits and herbs in it and still have a delicious drink. Throughout this book kombucha (see page 105) is used in multiple ways to make the most of its flavour profile: in dressings, as a fermenting agent and here as the main ingredient.

Serves: 2

Time taken: 10 minutes

For the rosemary syrup

1 rosemary sprig

Grated zest of 1 grapefruit

100g (3½oz) agave syrup

100ml (3½fl oz/scant ½ cup) filtered water

For the spiced salt

3 tbsp smoked sea salt

1 tsp dried chilli (pepper) flakes

1 tsp ground cinnamon

Juice of 1 large grapefruit

Juice of 1 lime

250ml (8½fl oz/1 cup) Kombucha (page 105)

Ice cubes, to serve

Rosemary sprig or twist of lime, to garnish

ROSEMARY SYRUP Put the rosemary, grapefruit zest, agave and water in a small saucepan over a medium heat and simmer for 10 minutes, stirring constantly, until the mixture thickens. Place a sieve over a small heatproof bowl, strain the mixture through the sieve and leave to cool.

SPICED SALT Mix the ingredients together on a small plate.

Use the lime or grapefruit juice to kiss the rim of two glasses and then dip the rims in the spiced salt mixture, moving the glasses around gently to make sure enough of the mixture sticks to them. Now prepare the glasses with some ice, you can choose how much you like to use. Add half of the grapefruit and lime juice to each glass and top up with kombucha then drizzle in 1–2 tablespoons of the rosemary syrup.

Store the syrup in a sealed container at room temperature for up to 1 month.

TIPS

– You can use any citrus here, just think about which herbs may pair well with your choice: this could be orange and thyme, bergamot and sage, blood orange and oregano, the possibilities are endless.

– The rosemary syrup can be used in many different drinks where sweetener is required, or even served simply as 1 tsp in a glass of sparkling water over ice.

GINGER & TURMERIC BUGS

Ginger and turmeric bugs are a simple starter culture for making fermented homemade sodas – I've also used them in the Fermented Ginger Cheesecake on page 163. Ginger roots are rich in yeasts and lactic acid bacteria, making them ideal for fermentation. Many of these beneficial organisms are found in the skin of the organic ginger plant, so it's best to leave the skin on. Fresh turmeric root can also be used in a similar way.

Makes: 500ml (17fl oz/about 2 cups)
Time taken: 1 week

2 tbsp grated organic fresh ginger or turmeric
    root (preferably with skin on)
2 tbsp organic cane sugar
2 tbsp filtered water

Equipment
500ml (17fl oz) sterilized glass jar
Clean muslin (cheesecloth)
Rubber band or string

Combine the grated ginger or turmeric, sugar and water in the sterilized glass jar. Cover with a cloth and seal with a rubber band or string and leave to ferment at room temperature. For the next 4–8 days, stir in an additional 2 tablespoons each of grated ginger or turmeric, sugar, and filtered water each day. Your ginger bug is ready when it produces noticeable bubbles and foam, makes a fizzing sound when stirred, and smells yeasty (similar to beer).

Serve with spoonfuls of sparkling water to make homemade soda, on herbal teas, or over ice topped up with kombucha. I personally love to take this as a shot or use it to ferment other things.

PRESERVED ORANGES

PRESERVED ORANGE HUMMUS

This recipe works for any citrus, but I love to use oranges as the salt and their sweetness make an interesting combination. I came across this idea on one of Rachel de Thample's classes and it opened my eyes to many possibilities. As I mention on page 100, you can save squeezed citrus for this process, as long as it is clean. If you do this, you will still need two whole fruits for their juice but can sub the rest for the skins. This way you can use what would otherwise be wasted and make an ingredient come to life in new ways.

Once you have completed the preserved oranges recipe, you can use them to create the following hummus recipe.

Makes: 500ml (17fl oz/about 2 cups)
Time taken: 10 minutes, plus 3 weeks fermenting time

5–6 organic oranges, washed
90ml (3fl oz/6 tbsp) sea salt
100ml freshly squeezed orange juice

FLAVOUR IDEAS
Cinnamon sticks, black peppercorns, bay leaves, coriander seeds, cloves

Equipment
500ml (17fl oz) glass jar, sterilized

Makes: 500g (1lb 2oz)
Time taken: 10 minutes

240g (8½oz) tinned chickpeas (garbanzo beans), drained and rinsed
40–60ml (1⅓–2fl oz/ 2¾–4 tbsp) aquafaba
1 Preserved Orange (roughly 100g (3½oz) (see left))
50ml (1½fl oz/3½ tbsp) freshly squeezed orange juice

80g (2¾oz) light tahini
2 tbsp extra virgin olive oil
2 roasted garlic cloves (optional)
½ tsp dried chilli (pepper) flakes
½ tsp cayenne pepper
4 pink peppercorns

Equipment
Food processor

Slightly trim the ends of the oranges and cut them lengthwise into quarters, stopping about 1cm (½ inch) before reaching the end, so the orange stays intact. Sprinkle 1–2 tablespoons of salt at the bottom of the clean jar. Fill the inside of each orange with salt and layer the oranges in the jar, adding additional salt between each layer (you do need a lot of salt!).

Press down on the oranges to release their juices and add orange juice as needed, so that the oranges are completely covered by liquid. Seal with the lid and allow the oranges to do their thing, at room temperature out of direct sunlight, for 3 weeks.

After this time the oranges will be soft, gooey and ready to use in dressings, salads, ice creams and more.

Put the chickpeas, aquafaba, preserved orange and orange juice in a food processor and process until smooth, then stream in the tahini and olive oil and add the garlic cloves (if using), chilli flakes, cayenne pepper and pink peppercorns at the end. Serve with fresh bread or as part of a salad plate or mezze.

The hummus will keep in the fridge in a sealed container for up to 1 week.

TIP – The juiciness of Preserved Oranges will vary a lot, so you will need to add more or less liquid to the hummus so it can easily process and become smooth (but not too thin).

THE CHEESE MODULE

A worldwide artisan addiction and the ultimate comfort food; for many, the one crux to their plant-based plate is cheese! Thankfully, our understanding of vegan cheeses has come on leaps and bounds in recent years and long gone are the days of rubbery imitations and substandard shop-bought versions of old classics.

Some people are resistant to using the word 'cheese'in the context of vegan alternatives to animal-based milk cheeses, but I think it helps us all understand what we are talking about. Calling vegan cheeses 'fermented nut spreads' or similar would definitely make them sound unappetizing even to the most happily plant-based of us. Fermented tofu has been used like cheese in Asia for centuries, and there are plenty of other historical examples of similar plant-based products. In modern plant-based cheese production, coconut and nuts are best known for their suitability and versatility in this fermentation process.

Notable innovators in this space include Miyoko Schinner, the founder of Miyoko's creamery in America and one of the pioneers of the vegan cheese movement, Willicroft cheese-makers in Amsterdam, known for their traditional techniques and bean-based cheeses, and Palace Culture in the UK who are making excellent Camemvert, Mouldy Goaty and even Sacre Bleu!

In this chapter we cover the fundamental skills for making nut-based cheeses using a simple fermentation process you can do at home. This process can become more advanced; but, however far you decide to expand your knowledge, mastering these basic foundations is key and will go a long way in upgrading your dairy-free delicacies.

MAKING A CHEESE BASE

First, a note on fermentation. Within this chapter I refer to using probiotic capsules, kombucha, sauerkraut or kimchi brine as your culture. Nuts and seeds need some help to ferment and these cultures are the cultures you will most likely find in your kitchen.

Live probiotics capsules (acidophilus) will give you the most reliable ferment but personally I like to use homemade cultures like kombucha, as you can make your own unique flavours that excitingly affect the end result. If you choose to use the brine from a vegetable ferment, bear in mind the flavour and your desired result.

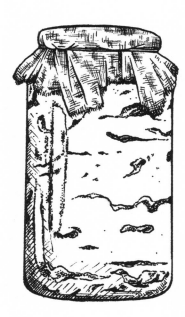

FERMENTED CASHEWS (CHEESE BASE)

This is a fermented nut or seed mixture that can be turned into cheese. You can simply flavour the mixture at the end to make a Cultured Sour Cream, use the mixture as a fermented cake base (see page 163) or continue the process to make a hard or soft cheese as in the recipes that follow.

Makes: 600g (1lb 5oz) Cheese Base

Time taken: 10 minutes, plus soaking and fermenting time

500g (1lb 2oz) nuts or seeds*, soaked (see pages 180–183 for soaking times) in filtered water, drained and rinsed

100ml (3½fl oz) filtered water

1 probiotic capsule, 2 tbsp kombucha or 2 tbsp sauerkraut/kimchi brine

Equipment

High-powered blender

Clean muslin (cheesecloth)

Rubber band or string

*Nuts and seeds won't all ferment in the same way: cashews and macadamia nuts are the most reliable, while higher-fat nuts, such as walnuts and seeds such as sunflower, are less stable. You can adapt the recipes here by using different nuts and seeds, but I would suggest mastering the basics and doing further research before you change it. Remember we are working with good and bad bacteria here, so use your senses to smell and see something before eating it.

Blend the soaked and rinsed nuts with the water in a high-powered blender until silky smooth. If the mixture gets hot while blending, leave it to cool before adding your chosen probiotic, as if the mixture is hot it will kill the bacterial culture and the mixture will not ferment.

Add the contents of the probiotic capsule (or your chosen probiotic) and blend briefly again, making sure the probiotic is thoroughly mixed through. Transfer the mixture to a shallow glass bowl, cover with muslin (cheesecloth) and secure with a rubber band/string, and leave at room temperature for at least 24–48 hours to start to ferment. You will know it is fermenting properly when you see the mixture start to aerate.

Once the mixture is fermented, look through the recipes on pages 114–118 to decide which type of cheese you would like to make.

TIP – If you have leftover cheese from any of recipes in this chapter, including this plain cheese base, and or simply want to make a crunchy cheese, spread the soft cheese mixture onto a baking sheet or dehydrator sheet to a thickness of 3–5mm (⅛–¼ inch) and either bake on the lowest temperature your oven will go until crisp, or dehydrate at 40°C/104°F overnight until crisp. Break the cheese into small pieces and use sprinkled over dishes or blend into a finer powder like grated parmesan.

MISO CHEESE

Making cheese is an exercise in flavour balance: every ferment will be different depending on the temperature of your space, the humidity in your area, how long you left the cheese to ferment, and of course the culture you decide to use. Use these recipes as guidance and taste to adjust them to your preference. 'Set' cheeses are great to use in salads, as a vegan cheese board or crumbled over roasted vegetables or pasta for a delicious flavour.

Makes: 1 cheese (roughly 6 servings, approximately 500g (1lb 2oz))
Time taken: 3 days

500g (1lb 2oz) Cheese Base made with cashews (page 113)
2–3 tbsp lemon juice
2 tbsp light miso
2 tbsp nutritional yeast (ground to a powder if needed)
½ tsp sea salt

Equipment
8–10cm (3½–4in) ring mould (or alternative mould shape)
Dehydrator (optional)

Once the Cheese Base fermentation is complete, mix all of the ingredients together in a clean bowl until totally smooth, taste and adjust the seasoning, adding more lemon juice, miso or yeast as required.

Line the ring mould (or any mould) with baking parchment. Press the flavoured mixture into the mould, making sure that the mixture is flat and well compacted into the shape of the mould. Freeze the mixture for 1–2 hours until set, remove the mould and paper then place in a dehydrator to dehydrate for 24–48 hours*: this process is what develops a rind.

Allow the cheese to cool completely, then store in the fridge, wrapped in baking parchment in a sealed container, for up to 1 month.

*If you don't have a dehydrator, use a fan oven at 110°C fan/130°C/260°F/gas mark ½ and cook for 2–4 hours until the cheese develops a rind.

AGED

SMOKED CHEESE

To develop their flavour these cheeses can go through an ageing process of anywhere from 1 week to 6 months, to enhance the flavour and evolve the texture. I find smoky flavours especially delicious in this recipe, but you could of course explore many, many different flavour profiles such as chilli cheese, turmeric cheddar or Kim-cheese using kimchi brine.

Makes: 1 cheese (roughly 6 servings, approximately 500g (1lb 2oz))

Time taken: 3 days

500g (1lb 2oz) Cheese Base made with cashews (page 113)

2 tbsp lemon juice

2 tbsp nutritional yeast (ground to a powder if needed)

1 tsp smoked paprika

½–1 tsp smoked sea salt

Equipment

8–10cm (3½–4in) ring mould (or alternative mould shape)

Dehydrator (optional)

Smoking gun (optional)

Once the Cheese Base fermentation is complete, mix all of the ingredients together in a bowl until totally smooth, taste and adjust the seasoning, adding more lemon juice or yeast as required.

Line a ring mould (or any mould) with baking parchment. Press the flavoured mixture into the mould, making sure that the mixture is flat and well compacted into the shape of the mould. Freeze the mixture for 1–2 hours until set, then place in a dehydrator to dehydrate for 24–48 hours*: this process is what develops a rind.

Allow the cheese to cool completely. If you have a smoking gun you can smoke the cheese at this point if you like (see page 80).

Store the cheese in the fridge, wrapped in baking parchment in a sealed container, and let it age for 1 week before eating. It will then keep in a sealed container in the fridge for 3 weeks.

*If you don't have a dehydrator, use a fan oven at 110°C fan/130°C/260°F/gas mark ½ and cook for 2–4 hours until the cheese develops a rind.

MACADAMIA ASH

This cheese has a creamy consistency with a more neutral flavour and less smooth texture than a cashew cheese. Macadamia nuts lend themselves to making a wonderful queso fresco or, in this case, a set cheese that can carry many different flavours. Here I have rolled the cheese in a kale ash. You could also dehydrate herbs to make herb powders, dry ferments to make toppings or use powdered spices to roll this style of cheese in.

Makes: 1 cheese (roughly 6 servings, approximately 500g (1lb 2oz))

Time taken: 3 days

500g (1lb 2oz) Cheese Base made with macadamia nuts (page 113)

1 tsp sea salt

1–2 tbsp lemon juice

1 tbsp nutritional yeast, ground to a powder if needed

½ tsp ground turmeric

For the kale ash

100g (3½oz/½ cup) kale, washed, dried and with the stems removed

½ tsp sea salt

Equipment

High-powered blender

Once the Cheese Base fermentation is complete, stir in the remaining ingredients until well combined. Place the mixture onto a piece of baking paper and roll to form a log. Freeze for at least 2 hours.

KALE ASH While the cheese is in the freezer, preheat your oven to 180°C fan/200°C/400°F/gas 6. Make the kale ash by laying the kale on a baking tray and placing it in the hot oven. Bake for 20 minutes, or until crisp and slightly burnt.

Cool and tip the kale into a blender. Add the additional ½ tsp sea salt and blend to a fine powder.

Once the cheese is set in the freezer, unwrap it and roll it in the ash. Store in a sealed container in the fridge until ready to serve. Keep in the fridge for up to 2 days once rolled, or up to 7 days if not rolled. It is best to roll just before serving.

COCONUT BOURSIN

This is another example of a fresh cheese, although this time nut free. Coconut yoghurt can be a great, pre-fermented base that you also find used in feta cheeses, labneh style cheese or here as a 'Boursin' style cheese with fresh herbs and garlic. This is a great recipe to serve as a dip, on toast, as a base loaded with grilled vegetables such as courgettes, or as part of a cheese board.

Makes: 1 cheese (roughly 6 servings, approximately 200g (7oz))

Time taken: 3 days

200g (7oz) coconut yoghurt, unsweetened
3 tbsp flat-leaf parsley, finely chopped
1 tbsp chives, finely chopped
½ garlic clove, minced
1 tsp Himalayan pink salt
1 tbsp apple cider vinegar

Equipment
Clean muslin (cheesecloth)

Put the coconut yoghurt in a large piece of clean muslin (cheesecloth) and hang it over a bowl with a sieve. Let the liquid drip for a couple of hours. Most liquid should come out, leaving you with a slightly set cheese.

Turn the cheese out of the cloth into a bowl and season with the parsley, chives, garlic, salt and apple cider vinegar. Place in a container in the fridge until ready to serve. It will keep in a sealed container in the fridge for up to 5 days.

CASHEW RACLETTE

This is a great recipe that I hope will open your eyes to the many possibilities of plant-based cheeses. This 'cheese' is not fermented but has a deep flavour because of the cooking process. You can serve this raclette as a shared starter, as part of a salad feast or use it as a topping to dishes where you are looking for a rich and creamy finish.

Makes: 2 cheeses (roughly 6 servings, 3 per cheese, approximately 500g (1lb 2oz))
Time taken: 1 hour, plus 1 day soaking time

500g (1lb 2oz) cashews, soaked for 4 hours in filtered water, drained and rinsed
2–4 tbsp filtered water (just enough to blend)
1 probiotic capsule or 2 tbsp kombucha
2–3 tbsp dry vegan white wine
1–2 tbsp nutritional yeast
2 tbsp lemon juice, to taste
Pinch of sea salt, or to taste

Equipment
High-powered blender
Clean muslin (cheesecloth)
10cm (4in) round moulds

Blend the rinsed cashews with the water in a high-powered blender until you get a silky smooth texture. If the mixture gets hot while blending, leave it to cool before adding your chosen probiotic, as if the mixture is hot it will kill the bacterial culture and the mixture will not ferment. Add the contents of the probiotic capsule (or the kombucha) and blend briefly again. Transfer the mixture to a shallow glass bowl, cover with muslin (cheesecloth) and leave at room temperature for at least 24 hours to culture. You will know it is fermenting properly when you see the mixture start to aerate.

Flavour the cashew mixture with the wine, nutritional yeast, lemon juice and salt. Line the round moulds with baking parchment. Portion the mixture into the moulds and leave it to set in the freezer for at least 1 hour to help them to hold their shape.

Preheat the oven to 200°C fan/220°C/425°F/gas 7. Turn out the cheeses into a small cast-iron pan and bake them for about 20 minutes until a nice crust is formed.

Top with paprika oil (see Smoked Salsa Macha page 31) and serve with toasted gluten-free bread.

THE MISSING INGREDIENT

THE ORIGINS OF OUR INGREDIENTS, CULTURAL IDENTITY & FOOD STORIES

By Arthur Potts Dawson

Chef, teacher and UN World Food Program Advocacy Chef

Every meal tells a story – and stories are told by cooks and chefs on plates every day all over the world.

The movement and migration of food items has deeply influenced regional culture, recipes, art, language, music and our beliefs, as well as survivability and resilience. With apples originating from Kazakhstan and Roman nettles marched into England by invading Roman troops, and similarly maize into Africa and tomatoes into Italy, appreciating that what we consider to be culturally significant cuisine may have been created from foods that have migrated is important.

Diet, nutrition and affordability play a huge role in health, and it is critical we understand that migrated foods have added significantly to local, regional and culturally identifiable diets. Plants and their migration around the world are the missing ingredient in our comprehension of the global foodscape that we live in.

Music, art, dance and spoken word can travel a great distance in seconds, but a flavour, a smell, an ingredient and a tangible experience can take days, weeks, months or even years to permeate a new environment and be culturally accepted. Nowadays food, recipes and cooking styles are instantly available online, but while the sound and sight of a dish can be transferred instantly, the smell, texture, taste and nutrition need to be tangibly experienced. Chefs and food allow cultural migration through the experience of a specific style, flavour, smell and fermentation. This leads to the wonderful opportunities of cultures learning from each other, lending flavours, sounds, style and colour, as well as bringing nutrition and health to homes, restaurants and communities all over the world, allowing the people of this planet to connect quickly to cultural migration. Now that we are digitally aware, it is paramount that we embrace all that food must give us in the physical and emotional sense.

The movement of people and food is the missing ingredient to everything we put onto our plates. It's important to keep growing, cooking and eating styles alive. Seed sharing and innovative and biodynamic farming systems, as well as more conventional farming, need support and improvement.

Grow, cook, eat and have fun using ingredients with awareness, consciousness and intention for the stories you too wish to share through your plates.

SOURCING YOUR FOOD

Here, I want to introduce you to a few different ways of sourcing your food. In an ideal world, seeking out local farmers' markets, shopping locally and avoiding large supermarkets is always going to be the most future forward way.

Most huge supermarkets as they are, unfortunately, cannot see us into the future as they are filled with processed foods, mass produced ingredients and fresh produce laced with pesticides from greenwashed farms.

Contrary to popular belief, farmers' markets and local growers are often cheaper and grow seasonal produce which will always be more nutrient dense and tasty than produce imported from further afield. If you do have to shop at supermarkets, try to only choose in-season produce, and if you can opt for organic, that's even better. The next step would be to visit your local farmers' market and buy fresh produce from there. Whether you are an individual or a business, building relationships with these growers will tend to lead to a more mutually beneficial option; it is key to building a strong support network for local growers at the same time as nourishing yourself and becoming more aware of what's in season when.

If you have the time to forage even better – it's FREE FOOD! But do educate yourself: forage with someone knowledgeable and also, most importantly, respect the 'forager's code' by taking only what you need and not uprooting plants.

Limitations on our time and budget, and where we live, affect our choices, but if we all made the effort to adjust our sourcing habits in any small way, what a different world it would be!

LOCAL

Local produce means food that is grown near to you, produce that is in season, abundant and pops up from the ground to give you what you need at a particular time of year. The benefits of eating seasonally are that it supports the growers in your area, provides you with the optimum nutrition and also encourages biodiversity into your diet, along with a healthy dose of inspiration, each time the seasons change.

ORGANIC

Organic ingredients are defined in the UK as '(of food or farming methods) produced or involving production without the use of chemical fertilizers, pesticides, or other artificial chemicals' by the Oxford English Dictionary. Of course, this way of growing is the original way – how things were done pre mass production and the normalizing of toxic pesticides and chemically altered produce. Organic produce can be more expensive to buy, but some may argue the chemically altered produce leads to larger costs long term, such as health implications, supporting corrupt systems and most vitally harming the microbiome of the earth – the soil! These costs, unfortunately, cannot be redeemed so easily.

When seeking out organic produce, talk to the growers if you can, as sometimes they may have not yet gone through a certification process but may already be growing food without pesticides and harmful chemicals.

BIODYNAMIC

'Biodynamic farming involves consulting a calendar on the phases of the moon and the alignment of planets', according to the Cambridge Dictionary. It may sound far out, but this is where farming has come from. Originally, we would have used common knowledge about moon phases, seasons and rituals to help our crops thrive.

In the UK, the term biodynamic came from Rudolf Steiner's lectures in 1924, which activated a worldwide movement, especially in agriculture, vineyards and gardens – which is most commonly where you will find the term used today - especially in the world of natural wines. The benefits of biodynamics are growing crops that are aligned with natural cycles and grown by people with a deep understanding of the world's ecosystem.

FORAGED

Foraging means to seek out wild food sources, plants that grow naturally and aren't cultivated in the way other crops are. This can include wild herbs, leaves and berries, and it can be incredible to learn how many different plants are abundant and available in your local area. Sometimes you will also find produce labelled as foraged or brands using foraged ingredients. Almost everywhere you will find savvy foragers who take people out on walks to learn about what plants are safe to pick and eat. Adding foraged food to your diet can greatly increase the diversity in your microbiome, which is key to gut health, it can inspire wild creativity in the kitchen, and also add fantastic flavour to your plates.

APPLE & WALNUT SALAD

Adapted from Arthur Potts Dawson's recipe from the Plant Academy's courses

Apples are considered one of the most ancient foods, looking back to the beginning of creation. They are thought to have over 7000 varieties, a quarter of which originated in the UK. Apples have huge potential in many dishes, and are used in countless essential ingredients, from vinegar to pectin, from cakes to salads. This recipe is adapted from Arthur Potts Dawson's recipe taught on Plant One, and is a humble ode to apples; we hope it inspires you to consider them in a new way.

Serves: 4 as a side salad or 2 as a main salad

Time taken: 15 minutes

Bunch of flat-leaf parsley

Bunch of chervil (optional)

A handful of foraged leaves and herbs, such as wild rocket (arugula), fat hen, wild garlic flowers or chervil (optional)

Bunch of chives (optional)

6 heads red or green chicory (endive), washed and dried

3 apples (mixed varieties)

300g (10½oz) Candied Walnuts (page 40)

100g (3½oz) Massaged Kale (page 48)

For the dressing

Zest and juice of 1 large lemon

90ml (3fl oz) olive oil

1 tbsp Dijon mustard

1 small garlic clove, minced

1 spring onion (scallion), finely sliced

1 tsp honey or agave

LEAVES Pick the herbs and cut the chives (if using) in half then cut the bottoms off the chicory heads and finely dice the base (depending on the variety of chicory you have this might look different). Put them in a serving bowl, reserving some of the chervil/chives to serve (if using).

DRESSING Whisk all of the ingredients together in a small bowl and then add this vinaigrette to the leaves.

ASSEMBLE AND SERVE Quarter and core the apples just before serving and slice the quarters into 5mm (¼ inch)-thick pieces – the longer the better for the look and feel of the salad. Add the apples to the salad with the walnuts. Add the massaged kale and mix well with your hands to make sure all of the leaves and herbs are coated with the dressing then arrange the salad onto plates. Garnish with the remaining chervil and chives.

WILD ROSTI

With Macerated Tomatoes, Sour
Cream & Foraged Leaves

Potatoes are grown and appreciated in culinary cultures on
every continent, with more than 500 varieties. They tend to fall
into two categories: waxy or floury. Get to know your spuds
and there are so many new flavours to explore. You need good
waxy potatoes to make a crispy rosti, but don't be limited by
standard supermarket spuds, go to a farmers' market and pick up
something different to see how they work out.

Serves: 2

Time taken: 1 hour

For the wild rosti

3 tbsp light olive oil

2 large potatoes* (about 200g/7oz), washed

1 carrot, washed

1 tsp sea salt

2 thyme sprigs, leaves picked

1 tsp dried oregano

For the macerated tomatoes

2 heirloom tomatoes

1 tsp sea salt

2 tbsp olive oil

For the tomato skin crisps

Tomato skins (from the macerated tomatoes)

1 tsp maple syrup

1 tsp olive oil

½ tsp sea salt or chilli salt

To serve

Cashew Sour Cream (page 33)

Selection of small foraged leaves like
    watercress, wild rocket (arugula) or wild
    mini kale

*There is a debate when making rostis about
    using waxy or floury potatoes. Waxy
    potatoes give more of a crunch, while floury
    potatoes create a lighter texture. I suggest
    you try the potatoes local to you in this
    recipe and see what you enjoy best.

WILD ROSTI Spiralize (or grate) the potato and carrot into a large bowl and sprinkle with the salt. Leave to sit for 10 minutes, for the salt to draw the water out of the vegetable.

MACERATED TOMATOES While the rosti veg are sitting, cut a cross in the bottom of each tomato, submerge them in hot filtered water for 2 minutes then place them in cold filtered water before carefully peeling away the skins. After peeling, save the skins for the tomato crisps. Cut the peeled tomatoes into elegant pieces – depending on your tomato, this could be small cubes or small moons. Sprinkle with the salt and leave to sit for 20 minutes.

TOMATO SKIN CRISPS Preheat the oven to 160°C fan/180°C/350°F/gas 4 and line a baking tray with baking paper. Coat the tomato skins in the maple syrup, oil and salt then lay them out on the lined baking tray. Bake for 15 minutes until crisp.

WILD ROSTI Thoroughly squeeze the water from the potatoes and carrots. You can use a clean tea towel to squeeze the liquid. Pour away the starchy, salty liquid. Return the potato and carrot to the empty bowl and add the herbs.

Heat a non-stick frying pan over a medium heat. Add the oil and add half of the rosti mixture, making it into a flat circle in the pan. Put a pan lid or small plate on top of it to make the shape and cook for 3–4 minutes on the first side then carefully flip it to cook the other side (you can also make one large, thicker rosti, if you have an ovenproof pan – bake for up to 15 minutes at 160°C fan/180°C/350°F/gas 4 until crisp on the outside and cooked through). Make sure the rosti is cooked through, crispy on the outside and soft in the middle and then turn off the heat.

To serve, pour away excess liquid from the tomatoes and drizzle with a couple of tablespoons of olive oil.

Serve the hot rosti on a plate topped with a circle of cream, followed by the macerated tomatoes and tomato skin crisps, and delicately cover with foraged leaves.

REALLY GOOD ROASTED ROOTS

Roasted roots are a classic dish in cafés and salad bars. To turn them into an interesting autumnal dish, I have added a tasty whipped bean butter, herb crisps and a savoury granola. This classic combination of a creamy base, hearty centre and crunchy topping is a real go-to for a satisfying plate (see page 170 for more about plating and designing dishes), though each element is fantastic alone too.

Serves: 2

Time taken: 40 minutes

For the whipped bean butter

2 tbsp olive oil

1 white onion, finely sliced

½ tsp smoked sea salt

2 tbsp Vegan Butter (page 148)

1 garlic clove, crushed

400g (14oz) tinned cannellini beans, drained
  – reserve the aquafaba (liquid from the tin)
  – and rinsed

¼ tsp cayenne pepper

¼ tsp freshly ground black pepper

Grated zest and juice of ½ lemon

For the roasted roots

2 tbsp olive oil

1–2 beetroots (beets), parsnips, turnips or
  carrots, cut into 2–5cm (1–2in) chunks

1 leek, or red or white onion, cut into 2–5cm
  (1–2in) chunks

1 courgette (zucchini) or small winter squash,
  cut into 2–5cm (1–2in) chunks

50ml (1½fl oz/3½ tbsp) filtered water

1 tsp sea salt

2 thyme sprigs

For the herb crisps

20g (¾oz) leaves such as nettles, nasturtiums
  or basil

3 tbsp light tahini

1 tsp tamari

1 tbsp olive oil

½ tsp cayenne pepper

50–80g (1¾–2¾oz) Savoury Granola (page 70)

WHIPPED BEAN BUTTER Heat the olive oil in a medium frying pan over a medium-low heat, add the sliced onion and the salt. Cook for 15 minutes until transparent, soft and starting to caramelize, then add the butter and garlic and cook for another 5 minutes. Turn off the heat and add the beans to a high-powered blender with the buttery onions. Start to blend on a low speed and add as much aquafaba as you need to help the mixture move – you're looking for a textured mash-like consistency. Add the spices and lemon zest and juice and blend once more to combine. Return to the pan ready to warm through before serving.

ROASTED ROOTS Preheat the oven to 180°C fan/200°C/400°F/ gas 6. Toss the vegetables in the oil on a baking tray then add the water (which helps with cooking). Sprinkle with the salt, add the thyme on top and roast for up to 30 minutes until cooked through and starting to caramelize at the edges.

HERB CRISPS Pick the leaves from the stems and set aside. In a small bowl mix the rest of the ingredients together to form a smooth paste. Line a large baking tray with baking paper, dip the leaves in the paste one by one and lay them on the lined tray, then bake at 180°C fan/200°C/400°F/gas 6 for 20 minutes, until crisp, turning halfway through.

Warm the whipped beans and spoon a circle of them on a plate, top with roasted roots, a spoonful of granola, and finally top with the herb crisps. You could add seasonal fresh herbs here too, if you like.

TIPS
- Store the herb crisps you don't use in a sealed container and enjoy as a snack!
- Try serving with crunchy toasted sourdough, or use as a filling for a sandwich or wrap.

STOVE-TOP FLAPJACKS

What happened to the good old-fashioned flapjack? This recipe is inspired by that forgotten classic, a mix of textured oats, fruits and seeds bound together with honey, tahini and melted coconut oil and cacao butter. These simple flapjacks are an ideal snack that you can spike with herbs, spices or adaptogens. I love to make them for a week when I am on the go, or if I need an offering for gathering with friends.

Makes: 5 medium flapjacks

Time taken: 30 minutes, plus 2 hours to set

50g (1¾oz) pumpkin seeds

50g (1¾oz) sunflower seeds

150g (5½oz) gluten-free rolled oats

50g (1¾oz) dried fruits (I use cranberries here), larger dried fruit may need chopping

30g (1oz) cacao butter

50g (1¾oz) coconut oil

50g (1¾oz) light tahini

40g (1½oz) honey, coconut nectar or maple syrup

10g (⅓oz) rosemary needles, finely chopped

½ tsp sea salt

Heat a large, deep frying pan over a medium heat. Add the seeds and oats and toast for a few minutes until the seeds start to pop and the oats are lightly golden. Add the dried fruits and stir to combine, then add the cacao butter and coconut oil and keep stirring the mixture while the oils melt, it is important everything is very well combined. Drizzle the tahini and honey over the mixture, sprinkle with the rosemary and salt and mix well again. Turn off the heat.

Line a tin or airtight plastic container (approximately 10 x 20cm/4 x 8 inches) lined with baking paper or cling film, being sure to cover the base and sides of the container. Add the mixture to the lined container and press down firmly to make sure the flapjacks hold together. Chill the mixture in the fridge for at least 2 hours, until set. Cut, serve and enjoy!

These flapjacks will keep in the fridge in a sealed container for at least 1 week, if they aren't eaten before then!

TIP – This recipe makes a great cheesecake base and you can swap the seeds for nuts or a different selection of seeds, or switch the sweetener if you prefer maple syrup or agave. You could even change the oats for rye, buckwheat or spelt flakes.

UNDERSTANDING ADAPTOGENS

Adaptogens are plants that have exceptional properties and have been proven to have a positive impact on our health. The Oxford Dictionary definition: 'a natural substance considered to help the body adapt to stress'. That is exactly what they do.

Adaptogens need to be taken in small doses, over a period of time, in order for you to feel their effects. They help us to adapt to stress in different ways, and they also adapt to each of us differently. Let's take reishi, for example, which is a medicinal mushroom known for its calming properties; it helps with sleep and also hormonal balance. I may take this mushroom and not physically feel anything but notice hormonal imbalances start to improve, someone else may find it helps them to sleep better, and a third person may feel their anxiety lessen.

Various cultures have used these ingredients for millennia. I believe these functional plants are the missing link in our overall health and can be a powerful tool in the kitchen. As chefs and cooks, we have the opportunity to introduce people to these ingredients and demonstrate how easy and enjoyable they can be to eat. When used in your daily life, adaptogens can open the world up to you in a new way, help ease psychological and physical issues and put the power in your hands in terms of not only how we live but our ability to thrive.

In this chapter I will teach you about the different types of adaptogens, how to consume them and how to incorporate them into your cooking, recipes and life. I will also cover plants that have 'super food' status, which I refer to as 'potent plants'.

NOTE - You will also find adaptogens in my first book *Mind Food*.

ADAPTOGENS & POTENT PLANTS

These are the adaptogenic and powerful plants we will be using in this chapter and a brief dive in to their health-giving properties.

These plants can be combined to make sense together: for example, if I am making a breakfast dish I may use cordyceps and bee pollen for long-lasting energy, or in the evening reishi and cacao to create a dreamy and relaxed state. It is so important to understand the feelings they invoke and the flavours that match.

Please note that all adaptogens have possible side effects. It's worth consulting a medical professional before introducing adaptogens if you are on medication, pregnant or breastfeeding, as some may not be safe.

TYPES OF ADAPTOGENS

Adaptogens are plants with incredible abilities to adapt to their surroundings and must be differentiated from potent plants. Adaptogens are unique in helping your body respond to stress, regulate the immune system and support adrenal health, amongst other things, which is useful when our bodies are stressed over a sustained period. In this adaptogenic category you have medicinal mushrooms, that I will dive in to on page 137, and also these adaptogens you can use in your food and life:

ASHWAGANDHA (AKA INDIAN GINSENG) an ayurvedic herb that can be helpful to reduce anxiety, stabilize blood sugar and help the body manage stress

RHODIOLA to reduce fatigue and support with resilience

GINSENG (AKA CHINESE/RED GINSENG) one of the most widely known plants that can be helpful in improving stamina and boosting energy

MACA a Peruvian root thought to give energy, support libido and contribute to hormonal balance

TULSI (AKA HOLY BASIL) may improve mental clarity, give balance and boost the immune system

POTENT PLANTS

I want to include some plants that are not adaptogens here, because of their powerful effects. These plants have a more consistent effect when used on a regular basis, and can have an impact whether used in cooking, used distilled (for example in an edible essential oil) or enjoyed in drinks. Some examples:

ROSEMARY for positive effects on memory

SAFFRON to boost your mood

LAVENDER for a sense of calm

CINNAMON for digestion

MATCHA for energy and antioxidant benefits

BEE POLLEN for energy and immunity

CACAO for heart-opening, energy and many more benefits

MEDICINAL MUSHROOMS

Medicinal mushrooms are now categorized as nutraceuticals (functional foods) for their ability to help prevent disease, treat illness and enhance the body's natural defence mechanisms. Naturally occurring beta-glucans in mushrooms are recognized by the immune receptors in our gut, which helps train our immune cells for various functions, including improving our physical resistance to external and internal stress.

Some examples (in addition to reishi and cordyceps mentioned on page 136):

LION'S MANE for focus
CHAGA for immunity
TREMELLA for skin
BIRCH POLYPORE for reducing inflammation
MAITAKE for insulin sensitivity
SHIITAKE for cardiovascular health

These mushrooms are most commonly found in tincture or powder form, can be used with heat and can be an amazing addition to many dishes. Try them infused into drinks, to enhance desserts, extracted into cooking or taken directly under the tongue. Unfortunately, there are lots of brands out there jumping on the bandwagon and selling low-quality low-dose mushrooms with false claims. Some of the few brands I trust at the moment in the UK are Bristol Fungarium, Wunder Workshop, KÄÄPÄ health and Oh My Shrooms.

CBD

CBD is the non-psychoactive component in cannabis and works with our endocannabinoid system to restore balance within our bodies, aid sleep, help reduce anxiety and soothe nerve disorders. CBD has gained in popularity around the world but still faces taboos and the same challenges as medicinal mushrooms, with many lower-quality products also on the market.

It can be hard to know how much to take, when to take it and which brands are the best. My tips is to choose your strength (the stronger you choose, the more medicinal it will be) and start gradually, with ½ a pipette once a day and working your way up to 1 pipette twice a day, morning and evening. CBD isn't cheap – if you choose a cheaper option, the product simply won't be as effective. I always buy CBD products from brands I know and trust who are transparent about their sources or are even producing it themselves. My favourites in Europe include Hempen, Huages, Wunder Workshop and Ho Karan.

In recipes it is best used without adding any heat, in salad dressings, raw desserts and drinks.

LESSON

When starting to take and use any of the plants and mushrooms in this category the most important thing is to start with just one at a time, normally taking ¼ teaspoon to start with and working up to ½ teaspoon. Try this one plant or mushroom for at least two weeks and then if you want to introduce more, do so in the same way. This way you will know which plant is working for you and how you are feeling. As you gain awareness and understanding you can confidently include and leave out different plants at different moments when you need them.

SAFFRON OATS

This sunny dish is spiked with saffron. Known as the happy herb, saffron is a potent plant because of its ability to lift your mood when consumed regularly. It is great in tea, in a stock, in pastas and in many savoury dishes, including this one. This recipe leads on from page 69 on grains making an oat-based risotto. The whole oats are cooked until soft with a saffron base for a dish that lifts your spirits and is kind on your body, too.

Serves: 2

Time taken: 1 hour, plus 1-2 days fermenting time

For the seed parmesan

100g (3½oz) Cashew Cream (fermented or unfermented will work, see page 113 for fermented)

50g (1¾oz) hemp seeds

1 tsp white miso

1 tbsp lemon juice

1 rosemary sprig, needles finely chopped

For the confit tomato and hemp oil

100g (3½oz) cherry tomatoes, washed and halved

50ml (1½fl oz/3½ tbsp) olive oil

1 stick rosemary, finely chopped

1½ tsp smoked sea salt

150ml (5fl oz/⅔ cup) hemp oil

Saffron infusion

400ml (14fl oz/1¾ cups) boiling filtered water

8 saffron threads

For the savoury saffron oats

2 tbsp olive or untoasted sesame oil

100g (3½oz) white onion, finely diced

½ tsp sea salt

1 garlic clove, finely chopped

150g (5½oz) oat groats, soaked overnight in filtered water with 1 tbsp apple cider vinegar, then drained and rinsed

1 tsp white miso

Edible leaves and flowers, to serve

SEED PARMESAN Blend the cashew cream with hemp seeds, white miso and lemon juice in a high-powered blender until smooth and then fold through the chopped rosemary. Spread the cheese onto a baking sheet or dehydrator sheet to a thickness of 3–5mm (⅛–¼ inch) and either bake on the lowest temperature your oven will go until crisp, or dehydrate at 40°C/104°F overnight until crisp.

Cool and then break the cashew cream into small pieces and store in an airtight continer until ready to use.

CONFIT TOMATO AND HEMP OIL Preheat the oven to 160°C fan/180°C/350°F/gas 4 and line a small baking tray with baking paper. Put the tomatoes on the lined tray, drizzle with the olive oil and sprinkle with the rosemary and salt. Roast for 45 minutes until beautifully soft and starting to caramelize. Let the tomatoes cool then blend them with the hemp oil in a blender until smooth. Store in the fridge until ready to serve.

SAFFRON INFUSION In a heatproof bowl, pour the boiling water over the saffron and leave to infuse for 10 minutes.

SAVOURY SAFFRON OATS Heat the oil in a deep frying pan over a medium–high heat, add the onion and salt and sauté for 5 minutes until translucent, then add the garlic and cook for a further minute. Cook the groats over a medium heat for 35 minutes, adding the saffron infusion a ladleful at a time until you have used all of the saffron infusion and the oats are al dente. Turn off the heat and add the miso.

To serve, place the oats on the plate with a spoonful of tomato oil, some fresh leaves and flowers, and finish with a few shards of the seed parmesan.

CBD SALAD

The dressing of this sumptuous salad is laced with CBD, and the salad includes candied seeds, massaged kale, crisp radicchio and a creamy base. When using CBD in any recipe, regulate the dose you want to take. When cooking for someone or eating this dish over a few days, remember how much you put in and regulate how much you are taking. You can't overdose on CBD, but it is always important to be aware of how much you are taking.

Serves: 2

Time taken: 30 minutes

1 batch of Cashew Cream (page 113)

1 batch of Massaged Kale (page 48)

1 batch of Candied Seeds (page 40)

6–8 radicchio leaves, washed and dried, to serve

For the dressing

100ml (3½fl oz/scant ½ cup) cold pressed olive oil

1 tbsp mild dried chilli (pepper) flakes

1 tsp hot smoked paprika

1 tsp sweet paprika

½ tsp smoked sea salt

Juice of 1 lemon (reserve the zest to serve)

2 tbsp wholegrain mustard

1 tsp honey or agave (optional)

CBD – your chosen dose (I use 1 pipette of 10% CBD) (optional)

DRESSING Put the oil, dry spices and salt in a small saucepan, bring to a simmer over a medium heat and cook for 5 minutes then turn off the heat and leave to infuse while you continue the other steps.

Prepare the cultured cashew cream, massaged kale and candied seeds as per the instructions.

To serve, finish the dressing by pouring the cooled oil into a large jar, adding the lemon juice, mustard, sweetener and CBD oil (if using) and shaking well to combine. Divide the cashew cream on one large or divide between plates, and top with massaged kale, radicchio and a sprinkling of the candied seeds, then drizzle the dressing over the leaves and sprinkle over the lemon zest.

Enjoy with bread, as part of a salad selection, with cooked grains or even add beans to the salad to create an even heartier meal.

ADAPTOGEN SPIKED CHOCOLATE

No recipe book of mine would come to life without a version of this recipe! I find great pleasure in making adaptogen-laced chocolate that supports how I want to feel on any given week. A version of this recipe appeared in my first book *Mind Food* and this new recipe has become a staple in my weekly routine and in my dessert recipes. The joy of it is how adaptable it can be as a snack, as an accent on a dessert, or even as a layer within one.

Makes: 1 small tray, serves 6

Time taken: 20 minutes, plus minimum 1 hour to set

100g (3½oz) vegan dark chocolate (75-90% cocoa), finely chopped

20g (¾oz) coconut oil

100g (3½oz) Nut or Seed Butter – here I used Candied Pecan Butter (page 41)

20g (¾oz) walnuts

30g (1oz) chia seeds

30g (1oz) hemp seeds

40g (1½oz) dried fruits – here I used goji berries and raisins

½ tsp smoked sea salt (or regular sea salt)

1 tsp adaptogen powder – here I used a combination of lion's mane and maca

½ tsp ground cinnamon (or vary other spices)

1–2 tbsp yacon syrup, or your chosen sweetener (optional, depending on which chocolate and nut butter you use)

Dried flowers or extra seeds, to garnish

Bring a small saucepan of filtered water to a simmer. Put the chocolate and coconut oil in a heatproof bowl and place the bowl over the simmering water, making sure the water isn't touching the bowl. Stir gently until the chocolate and coconut oil have melted and combined. Remove the mixture from the heat, and let it cool a little. When it's just warm, add the nut or seed butter and mix to completely combine. Add the nuts, seeds, fruit, salt, adaptogens, spices and sweetener (if using) and stir to completely combine.

Line a small tray or airtight plastic container with baking paper, making sure the surface and sides where you plan to pour the chocolate are covered. You can choose whether you want to make thinner shards (as pictured) or a deeper bar for this recipe, so choose the size of the tray or container you use accordingly. Pour the mixture into the lined container and sprinkle with dried flowers or extra seeds before placing in the fridge for at least 1 hour until completely firm.

Portion up the Adaptogen Spiked Chocolate and keep in a sealed container in the fridge for up to 2 weeks.

TIP – This recipe can be adapted to have endless different flavours by using interchangeable combinations of nut butters, seeds, nuts and fruits.

HOT CHOCOLATE TONIC

A simple way to use adaptogens is in drinks, from smoothies and cocktails to teas and hot drinks, as most of these ingredients come in tincture form and most of the powders mix well, especially in smoothies. Thinking creatively, you can then use these adaptogen laced liquids, such as the chaga tea here, as bases to flavour and infuse other things, such as a part of a dessert or syrup, for instance. Adaptogen options are provided below.

Serves: 1
Time taken: 1 hour and 10 minutes

Chaga tea
1 piece of chaga*
1l boiling filtered water
3 cardamom pods
2 star anise
4 cloves

Chocolate tonic
100ml (3½fl oz/scant ½ cup) Plant Milk (page 38)
100ml (3½fl oz/scant ½ cup) chaga tea
2-3 tbsp raw cacao powder
1-2 pitted dates
A pinch of sea salt

Adaptogen options
Lift ¼ tsp maca powder with ¼ tsp cayenne pepper
Sooth ¼ tsp reishi powder or tincture with ¼ tsp ground cinnamon
Balance ¼ tsp ashwagandha and ¼ tsp ground cloves
Focus ¼ tsp lion's mane powder or tincture and 4–5 rosemary needles

Equipment
High-powered blender

*Chaga in its raw form looks like a dark rock and is incredibly potent and a very cost effective ingredient. By boiling chaga in hot water you extract its medicinal properties and flavour. You can reuse it up to 3 times, freezing the chaga itself in between uses.

CHAGA TEA Add the chaga, boiling water and spices to a large saucepan and boil for 1 hour until you have a deep brown liquid. Remove the chaga and spices and use straight away or cool and store in the fridge for up to 5 days.

CHOCOLATE TONIC Blend all of the ingredients in a high-powered blender until smooth. Serve cold over ice, or warm through in a saucepan on a low heat.

Serve and feel the desired effects. You can add rosebuds for a finishing touch (pictured).

TIP – Blend this hot chocolate tonic with avocado to turn it into a quick mousse, or freeze into chocolate ice cubes to make it into a granita, served with another milk poured over the top. You can also blend it into a smoothie.

GLUTEN-FREE BAKING

Baking is usually one of the first cooking experiences we have, and bakes are often the first foods we fall in love with. Many can be made both vegan and gluten-free with great results but becoming familiar with alternatives for the 'usual' ingredients is key.

In this chapter I will break down the purpose of each of these ingredients and their properties so you can better understand baking the plant-based and gluten-free way. Butter, flour and liquids are covered on the following pages, but some other crucial components that help give personality to your bakes, on top of the flavours you add, include:

Sugar: Sugar delivers the delicious sweetness in baked goods, but it is also what makes a cookie crispy, helps sponges store well and makes an icing fluffy. In the Plant Academy pantry, you will often see rapadura (whole cane) sugar, coconut sugar, maple syrup and honey, which we use as ethical sweet alternatives to refined cane or white sugar.

Salt: This should not to be forgotten in any bake and is important for enhancing and balancing savoury and sweet baked goods.

Raising agents: Bicarbonate of soda (aka Baking soda) is a pure leavening agent used to make things rise. In plant-based baking you may also use apple cider vinegar alongside baking soda, to create a lightness in a bake and you can also use acidic ingredients such as lemon and even cacao to enable this rise. Baking powder is less strong than bicarbonate of soda as it is bicarbonate of soda pre-mixed with a dry acidic ingredient that is there to make the bake rise without anything else. You will often find both of these ingredients in sweet gluten-free bakes, and they help dictate the end result of your bake.

THE KEY INGREDIENTS

The following techniques show you how to create homemade, plant-based versions of three of the key ingredients in baking.

Fat: Butter (or sometimes oil) binds ingredients together, carries the flavour through the bake and helps it retain moisture and ensure all the ingredients to cook through properly. Plant-based butters are normally made of a mix of coconut and olive oil with a nut or creamy element. Olive oil or a neutral oil such as grapeseed is also often used.

Binders: In order to hold ingredients together, something rich in protein is often added to the mix. In classic baking this may be eggs, and in plant-based baking the equivalent binding ingredient can be a mixture of flax seeds and water, aquafaba, fermented batters or yoghurt.

Flour: Gluten-free flours are the substance of pastries and sponges and define how soft or crisp they are, as well as the flavour and texture. A mix of flours is often used in gluten-free baking to create the desired texture and could include flours such as rice, buckwheat, corn, potato, sorghum, and tapioca.

There is a common misconception about flour. My friend Nancy Drew (@consciouscooking_), a plant-based chef and baker, explains that flour does not simply mean milled wheat flour, as people normally assume. Flour is the structure of the product after it has been milled or blended which can apply to many grains and even nuts and seeds. So in gluten-free baking, flour is still there to structure different bakes but we use a much wider variety than you may be used to so we can create flavours and structures in a gluten-free way.

TECHNIQUE 1

BUTTER

Butter is defined by the Oxford English Dictionary as 'a pale yellow edible fatty substance made by churning cream and used as a spread or in cooking'. There is so much controversy around using the word 'butter' for a plant-based food, but we are talking about an ingredient with the same uses and purpose, apart from this time we are using milk made from a plant. This is a simple way to make butter. Note that this is different to the nut butters explored on page 41.

Makes: 500g (1lb 2oz)
Time taken: 20 minutes

100ml (3½oz/scant ½ cup) Plant Milk (page 38), such as almond, cashew or macadamia
150ml (5fl oz/⅔ cup) light olive oil

150ml (5fl oz/⅔ cup) coconut oil, odourless
40g (1½oz) fermented cashew cream (page 113)
1 tsp apple cider vinegar
1 tsp sea salt

Equipment
High-powered blender

Blend all the ingredients together in a blender, pour into a wide metal bowl and place over a larger bowl of iced water. Whisk consistently until the mixture has a creamy and set consistency. This will usually take 10–15 minutes.

Store in a sealed container in the fridge for up to 1 week.

TECHNIQUE 2

FLAX 'EGG'

Mixing ground flax seeds with water creates a gel. Flax seeds work brilliantly as a binder because of their ability to produce this particular texture. Avoid buying pre-ground flax seeds as they go rancid so quickly and use golden flax seeds rather than brown flax are they are more gelatinous.

Makes: 1 flax 'egg'
Time taken: 15 minutes

1 tbsp freshly ground golden
   flax seeds
1 tbsp filtered water

Whisk the flax and water together and leave to stand for 10 minutes. Once made a gel, it will remain that way and can be made ahead of time.

TIP – Consider the liquids you use in baking, such as water, tea, infusions, plant milk or even yoghurt. These ingredients give moisture as well as flavour, texture, colour and volume. This component adds a specifc quality to all bakes and gives more or less character as needed.

TECHNIQUE 3

GLUTEN-FREE FLOUR BLENDS

Gluten-free flours are a huge topic – they deserve a book of their own – but here are some base recipes for you to explore. Gluten-free flours can be categorized, depending on how dense they are, as light, 'starchy' flours, such as tapioca; medium flours, such as bean or oat; or heavy flours, such as almond or buckwheat. It is important flour blends have a mix of these as you can see in the examples below. For people who don't regularly bake, it may be more convenient to use good-quality gluten-free flour blends, but if you are interested in making your own, I recommend the following.

Makes: 1kg (2lb 4oz) jar
Time taken: 10 minutes

Sponge blend
320g (11¼oz/2½ cups) tapioca flour (binder and gives stretch)
240g (8½oz/1 cup) oat flour (sweet and flavoursome)
240g (8½oz/1 cup) sorghum flour (nutty and rich flavour)
1 tsp xanthan gum (stabilizing and thickening)

Makes: 500g (1lb 2oz) jar
Time taken: 10 minutes

Biscuit blend
200g (7oz/scant 1 cup) chestnut, buckwheat or sorghum flour (nutty flavour)
160g (5oz/1 cup) tapioca starch (binder and gives stretch)
120g (4oz/¾ cup) brown rice flour (high in fibre, similar to wholewheat flour)
2 tsp baking powder (stabilizing)
2 tsp bicarbonate of soda (rising agent – optional)

BUCKWHEAT PUMPERNICKEL

This is a fantastically funky bread that at its most simple only needs three ingredients: buckwheat groats, water and salt. You can make the fermented batter into many different bakes, such as a flatbread, or a seedy loaf as in this recipe. This is an example of a minimal ingredient gluten-free bake that needs no complications, or flours but is a great option for those who avoid gluten as well as those who love delicious bread!

Makes: 1 medium-sized loaf, serves 12

Time taken: 1 hour, plus 2–3 days fermenting time

500g (1lb 2oz) whole unroasted buckwheat groats

1 tbsp sunflower seeds, soaked for 30 minutes in hot filtered water then rinsed

1 tsp caraway seeds, lightly toasted

1 tsp smoked sea salt

2 tbsp molasses

Olive oil, for greasing

Equipment

2lb (900g) loaf tin

High-powered blender

Place the buckweat in a bowl covered with room temperature filtered water, cover the bowl with a cloth and leave to soak for 24 hours.

Rinse the buckwheat thoroughly and blend in a high-powered blender with 125ml/4fl oz/½ cup room temperature filtered water until mostly smooth. Ferment in a glass bowl, covered at room temperature, for 24 hours.

The next day, soak the sunflower seeds in filtered water and toast the caraway seeds. Fold the seeds through the fermented buckwheat with the salt and molasses.

Grease the loaf tin with 1–2 tbsp olive oil and line with baking paper if the tin you are using is not non-stick. Transfer the buckwheat mixture to the loaf tin and leave your loaf to ferment for a further 12-24 hours, covered at room temperature, until risen by at least a quarter.

Preheat the oven to 180°C fan/200°C/400°F/gas 6.

Bake the loaf in the oven for 30 minutes, until all sides are crisp and the loaf is cooked through. To test this, turn it out and tap the bottom – it should sound hollow. Once cooked, rest in the tin for 10 minutes and then cool on a wire rack. Once cooled completely, slice as you need it and serve with your chosen toppings (butter or hummus work well).

Store this bread wrapped in baking paper in a sealed container for up to 4 days, or freeze for up to 1 month.

TIP – If you don't have molasses, use date syrup or make it plain, with a pinch of sea salt, it is still delicious.

ALMOND, PEANUT & CACAO COOKIE SANDWICHES

Over the years I have become a little obsessed with cookie sandwiches. They are like a playground of flavour combinations and textures; they can be iced or warm, and suit any occasion. These cookies are purposefully soft and contain a little less sugar than a crunchy cookie, to help you to eat the cookie sandwich easily. They freeze well and are so good you can eat them almost straight out of the freezer.

Makes: 10 cookie sandwiches

Time taken: 1 hour

For the almond butter cookies

150g (5½oz) Vegan Butter (page 148)

80g (2¾oz) thick coconut yoghurt

50g (1¾oz) smooth almond butter

½ tsp sea salt

150g (5½oz) coconut sugar

120g (4¼oz/1 cup) gluten-free flour (I love to use half chestnut flour and half gluten-free flour – which turns out well, but any good gluten-free flour blend works)

120g (4¼oz/1 cup) gluten-free self-raising flour

100g (3½oz) vegan dark chocolate (75–80% cocoa), roughly chopped into small pieces

For the whipped peanut butter

100g (3½oz) smooth peanut butter

100ml (3½fl oz/scant ½ cup) Plant Milk (page 38)

1 tbsp maple syrup

3 tbsp coconut oil, melted

½ tsp smoked sea salt (if the peanut butter is not already salted)

For the chocolate ganache

375g (12½fl oz/1½ cups) cashew cream (page 113, but omit the setting agent and replace with dark chocolate)

100g (3½oz) vegan dark chocolate (75–80% cocoa), melted

Pinch of sea salt

Equipment

High-powered blender

Piping bag

Whisk, electric or manual

ALMOND BUTTER COOKIES In a large mixing bowl whisk together the vegan butter, coconut yoghurt, almond butter, salt and sugar until well combined and lighter in colour. Sift in the flours and fold them through the mixture, then once they are almost combined fold in the chocolate chips. Chill the cookie dough in the fridge for 30 minutes.

WHIPPED PEANUT BUTTER Whisk the peanut butter and plant milk in a medium mixing bowl to make a smooth paste. Add the maple syrup, coconut oil and salt and mix once more. Set aside.

CHOCOLATE GANACHE Put the cashew cream in a blender and start to blend, then stream in the melted chocolate while the motor is running until they have combined. Add the salt and mix once more. Set aside. (You can whisk them together by hand if you prefer, but make sure the cashew cream is at room temperature and not solid, or the chocolate will seize.)

Preheat the oven to 180°C fan/200°C/400°F/gas 6 and line a baking tray (or two) with baking paper. Roll the chilled cookie mixture into 20 balls the size of an avocado stone, place them on the tray(s), allowing enough room for them to slightly spread, and bake for 11 minutes until golden brown. Remove from the oven and leave them to cool completely on the tray.

To make the sandwiches, lay out the cookies, half facing up and half facing down. On each of the cookies facing down add 1 teaspoon of the whipped peanut butter. Pipe the chocolate ganache around the whipped peanut butter and then put the top on the sandwich. Eat straight away or set in the fridge before eating.

The cookies will keep in a sealed container in the fridge for up to 3 days or are even better frozen for up to 1 month.

TIP – Depending on your peanut butter you may need a little more or less milk. As you start stirring, the mix should come together to make a smooth paste that holds on a spoon and, when you add the remaining ingredients, should still be smooth and thick. If when you add the oil the mix doesn't come together, add a splash more filtered water.

MEDICINAL MUSHROOM GATEAUX

This is one of my all-time favourite recipes. It came about when I was inspired by our guest chefs on the Plant Two course. We had been cooking sponges with Kirk Haworth and making delicious mushroom 'Twix'-style bars with Ayelen Martinez and this recipe was a byproduct of what they were teaching. With layers of mushroom sponge and caramel enrobed in chocolate, nothing beats the finesse of an adaptogen-spiked layered sponge.

Makes: 5 small cakes

Time taken: 1 hour

For the lion's mane sponge

50g (1¾oz) coconut sugar

¼ tsp bicarbonate of soda (baking soda)

120g (4¼oz/1 cup) gluten-free self-raising flour
or Sponge Blend (p149)

20g (¾oz) cornflour (cornstarch)

1 tbsp lion's mane powder (or mushroom
powder of your choice)

1 tbsp lemon juice

3 tbsp olive oil, plus extra for greasing

3 tbsp maple syrup

1 tsp vanilla extract

200ml (7fl oz/scant 1 cup) Plant Milk (page 38)
(almond, pumpkin and hazelnut work well)

For the walnut caramel

1 tbsp filtered water

50g (1¾oz) cacao butter

1 tsp chaga powder or tincture (optional)

100g (3½oz) coconut nectar

100g (3½oz) roasted Walnut Butter (page 148,
or you can use another nut butter here if you
prefer)

¼ tsp vanilla extract

½ tsp ground cinnamon

Pinch of sea salt

For the chocolate coating

100g (3½oz) cacao paste

60g (2¼oz) coconut oil (deodorized*)

2 tbsp maple syrup or honey

½–1 tsp tamari

To serve

5 fresh blueberries

Candied Cacao Nibs (page 40 (optional))

Equipment

High-powered blender

*This is a coconut oil without the flavour, useful
for recipes where the coconut flavour is not
required but you still need a setting agent.

LION'S MANE SPONGE Preheat the oven to 160°C fan/180°C/ 350°F/gas 4. Mix the dry ingredients together in a large bowl. Add the lemon juice, olive oil, maple syrup and vanilla, then gradually add the plant milk, mixing with a spatula then a whisk until smooth and shiny.

Line a flat, lipped baking tray with baking paper and grease it lightly with oil so the sponge doesn't stick. Pour the sponge mix into the lined tin – it should be about 5mm (¼ inch) thick. Bake in the oven for 8 minutes, turning the tray after 4 minutes so it bakes evenly. Remove from the oven, leave in the tray for 10 minutes and then turn out to cool completely.

WALNUT CARAMEL Blend all the ingredients in a high-powered blender until smooth, set aside.

CHOCOLATE COATING Melt the cacao paste and coconut oil in a saucepan over a low heat or on a double boiler. Remove from the heat and whisk in the remaining ingredients. Pour into a shallow bowl until ready to use. Use as soon as possible after making for the best result.

To assemble, cut the sponge into 15 even squares, circles or rectangles. Layer the sponge with caramel, making three layers, and leave to set in the fridge for 15 minutes, then pour over the chocolate coating and garnish with the blueberries. Set again for 10 minutes in the fridge before eating.

This cake will keep in a sealed container the fridge for 3 days.

RAW DESSERTS

Raw desserts were my first portal into the wonderful world of decadent plant-based food. When we adjust our diets, we may think that we will have to succumb to not having our favourite treats anymore. I had made my peace with the idea of never having an indulgently iced cupcake or silky-smooth chocolate cheesecake, but then I found out about the realm of raw desserts.

Raw food is food that is not heated over 42°C (108°F). In the raw food movement techniques like sprouting, activating and dehydrating are more commonplace because they do not exceed that temperature but enhance texture and flavour, and make ingredients easier to digest in a useful way. They were originally popularized by Ann Wigmore and Matthew Kenney and show us how to use natural ingredients in a minimally processed way with great effects.

This is another area where convenience has crept in. But why use a store-bought oat-based cream filled with stabilizers and vegetable oils when the homemade version would be quick, delicious and more cost efficient? We do not need to buy into big brand products that take creativity out of our hands and make the end result less delicious.

I believe this is the most important part of the plant-based pastry and desserts landscape. Once we understand the techniques for making a raw Chantilly, fermented cream or a simple biscuit base, these can complement cooked techniques to create a more interesting end result. In this chapter, you will see ways of including these raw techniques in recipes that merge raw thinking with current creative ideas to make caramels, chocolates and cheesecakes.

SWEET CREAMS & CARAMELS

BASE RECIPE

CASHEW CREAM

BASE RECIPE

EMULSIFIED CREAM

Cashew creams are known for their versatility and creaminess. Soaked and rinsed cashews are blended into a lightly sweetened and flavoured single or double cream, or you can add setting agents like coconut oil or cocoa butter to make Chantilly cream, clotted cream or mascarpone cream. Use half cashews and half coconut yoghurt for a lighter end result.

You can also use nut or seed butters as a base for a cream. This technique involves usually 1:1 nut or seed butter and liquid (which could be a plant milk or cooled tea), some liquid sweetener, flavourings and salt. Blend the nut butter and liquid together to make a thin cream then use cacao butter, coconut oil or melted chocolate to emulsify through the mixture and create a set cream to varying consistencies.

Makes: 750g (1lb 10oz)

Time taken: 1 hour

200g (7oz) cashews, soaked for 4 hours, drained and rinsed
200ml (7fl oz/scant 1 cup) Plant Milk (page 38), cooled tea or coffee
80–100ml (2¾–3½fl oz/scant ½ cup) liquid sweetener, such as maple syrup, honey or agave
¼ –½ tsp ground spices,

such as vanilla, cinnamon or ginger
1–3 tbsp superfood powders such as cacao, turmeric or matcha
¼–½ tsp salt, for example sea salt, white miso or pink Himalayan salt
150ml (3½fl oz/ cup) coconut oil, melted
50g (1¾oz/ cup) cacao butter, melted

Makes: 650g (1lb 7oz)

Time taken: 1 hour

100g (3½oz) Nut or Seed Butter (page 41)
200ml (7fl oz/scant 1 cup) Plant Milk (page 38)
75g (2½oz) liquid sweetener, such as maple syrup, honey or agave

¼–½ tsp salt, for example sea salt, white miso or pink Himalayan salt
80ml (3½fl oz/⅓ cup) coconut oil, melted
80g (3½oz/⅓ cup) cacao butter, melted
80g (3½oz/⅓ cup) vegan dark chocolate (80% cocoa), melted

Blend the first set of ingredients in a high-powered blender until silky smooth. Decide on the amount of liquid sweetener by taste. Then stream in the melted coconut oil and cacao butter. These fats are your setting agent and an essential part of this recipe. Make sure they are blended through the mix but don't over process them as the coconut oil especially will turn rancid if it overheats.

TIP – Cashews are also easily fermented, as in Fermented Ginger Cheesecake (see page 163).

Follow the same instructions as for Cashew Cream.

TIP – Emulsified creams can be nut free by using seeds, and you can also use these techniques with beans instead of cashews. Avocado can be a fantastic nut-free cream base, especially when combined with vegan chocolate or lime, and if you're in a region where fresh coconut is available, it creates endless possibilities for creams, yoghurts and ice creams.

BASE RECIPE

CARAMELS

Caramels come to life in many ways in plant-based desserts, from quick and soft date caramels to dulce de leche-style cooked caramels and raw set caramels. The principle is very much the same as in classic baking. Caramels consist of sugars and fats that caramelize into something rich and wonderful. These caramels can be used as part of a recipe, like in the nut butter bars on page 166, or as a sauce. Here are some base recipes for you to explore.

Date caramel   Makes: 400g (14oz) Time taken: 15 minutes

200g (7oz) pitted dates, soaked for 10 minutes, drained (keep the water)
100g (3½oz) Nut or Seed Butter (page 41, such as almond, tahini or peanut)
¼–½ tsp sea salt
½ tsp vanilla extract
100g (3½oz) coconut oil, melted

Blend the drained dates in a high-powered blender until very smooth, adding a little of the date soaking water as needed. Add the nut or seed butter and blend again, making sure it is well combined. Add the vanilla and coconut oil and blend again. This caramel can be used as a sauce or even piped onto a cheesecake.

Coconut sugar caramel   Makes: 500g (1lb 2oz) Time taken: 1 hour

1 x 400ml (14fl oz) tin of coconut milk
100g (3½oz/¾ cup) coconut sugar
1 tsp sea salt

Put all the ingredients in a heavy saucepan and cook on a low heat for 1 hour, stirring often and reducing to a gorgeous golden caramel. This caramel is ideal as a pourable sauce served hot or cold or used as a liquid sweetener.

Set caramel   Makes: 400g (14oz) Time taken: 10 minutes

95g (3⅓oz) coconut oil
80g (2¾oz) dark tahini
70g (2½oz) cacao butter, melted
40g (1½oz/4 tbsp) powdered rapadura (whole cane) sugar
½ tsp sea salt
100ml (3½fl oz/scant ½ cup) cold filtered water

Blend all the ingredients except the water in a high-powered blender until smooth, then stream in the water while the motor's running to make a thick caramel. This caramel is ideal as a layer in a cheesecake or a tart filling in it's own right.

RAW CHEESECAKE

This is my ultimate method for making a great raw cheesecake. If you've seen my desserts before, you will know that I love to work in layers. With a rich biscuit base, caramel or chocolate ganache centre and creamy topping, they are always topped with a crunch! The key part of this recipe is the adaptable biscuit base that you can use to make a variety of flavours and also add many different toppings.

Makes: 1 x 20cm (8in) round cake – serves 12

Time taken: 1 hour, plus 4–6 hours to set

For the biscuit base

150g (5½oz) gluten-free rolled oats

100g (3½oz) nuts or seeds, roasted or raw

1–2 tsp ground spices (such as cinnamon, cardamom or ginger) and/or adaptogens (such as maca, lucuma, cacao or medicinal mushrooms)

80g (2¾oz) pitted dates, coconut sugar or liquid sweetener, such as honey, maple syrup or agave

1 tsp sea salt or smoked sea salt

60ml (2fl oz/4 tbsp) filtered water

60ml (2fl oz/4 tbsp) coconut oil or cacao butter, melted (or olive oil if you want a softer base)

For the filling

Caramel (page 159) or Chocolate Ganache (page 153)

For the Cashew Cream or Emulsified Cream (page 158)

Candied Seeds (page 40), to serve

Equipment

High-powered blender or food processor

20cm (8in) springform tart tin

BISCUIT BASE Toast the oats, nuts or seeds for the best flavour. Heat a large frying pan over a medium-low heat, then toast the oats, nuts or seeds briefly, to lightly release their aroma. Put the oats, nuts or seeds and your chosen adaptogens or spices in a blender or food processor to form a fine flour (you can reserve some of the nuts or seeds and add them later if you want more texture). Add the pitted dates, coconut sugar or liquid sweetener and blend again. Stream in the water and melted coconut oil or cacao butter while the motor's running until the dough comes together. It should form a ball without cracking – if it's too dry, add 1–2 tablespoons more filtered water and blend again.

Line the base of the springform tart tin with baking paper. Press the biscuit dough into the base of the tin, making sure it is about 1cm (½ inch) thick, and chill in the fridge to set while you make the other elements of the cheesecake.

Make the caramel or chocolate ganache and pour it directly onto the biscuit base. Leave to set until set to touch (this should be around 1 hour in the fridge).

CASHEW CREAM/EMULSIFIED CREAM Pour this over the set caramel or chocolate ganache. Place back in the fridge to set for up to 4 hours. Keep any leftover cream in an airtight container or piping bag in the fridge for plating.

To serve, carefully remove the cheesecake from the tin and place it on a plate or chopping board. Cut it into 12 pieces, add your toppings and dig in. The cheesecake keeps for up to 1 week in the fridge, or 1 month in the freezer.

FLAVOUR IDEAS

SALTED CARAMEL AND POPCORN CHEESECAKE: Toasted oat base, tahini, mascarpone, miso, butterscotch and popcorn

MATCHA CHEESECAKE: Lemon biscuit base, matcha white chocolate ganache, matcha cream and berries

SMOKED CHOCOLATE CHEESECAKE: Toasted hazelnut biscuit base, smoked dark chocolate ganache, milk chocolate cream finished with smoked sea salt

FERMENTED GINGER CHEESECAKE

Cashew cheesecakes are a classic in the world of plant-based desserts. Cashews make a fine cream, and are one of the most effective ways to make a mascarpone-style cream, particularly. This tart used the power of fermentation to give the dessert a more complex flavour (and also make the nuts easier to digest). This cheesecake also has a cooked biscuit base, to create an interesting, delicious tart that stands apart from the crowd!

Makes: 1 x 20cm (8in) round or square cake –
serves 12

Time taken: 1 hour, plus minimum 4 hours to set

For the fermented cashew base

200g (7oz) cashews, soaked for 4 hours in
    filtered water, then drained and well rinsed

150ml (5½fl oz/⅔ cup) filtered water

50ml (1½fl oz/3½ tbsp) Ginger Bug (page
    108. You could also use ginger or plain
    Kombucha, page 105)

For the chestnut biscuit base

100g (3½oz/⅔ cup) chestnut flour, plus extra
    for dusting

150g (5½oz/1¼ cups) gluten-free flour blend

1 tsp sea salt

2 tbsp coconut sugar

180g (6½oz) Vegan Butter (page 148) or
    coconut oil, cut into small cubes

80g (2¾oz) thick coconut yoghurt

For the ginger cream

1 x quantity Fermented Cashew Base (above)

100ml (3½fl oz/scant ½ cup) almond milk

Zest and juice of 1 large lemon

75ml (2½fl oz/⅓ cup) honey or agave

20g (¾oz) piece of fresh ginger, peeled and
    grated

1 tsp ground ginger

2 tsp ground turmeric or 2 tbsp fresh turmeric
    juice

¼ tsp cayenne pepper

1 tsp vanilla extract

½ tsp sea salt

70g (2½oz) cacao butter, melted

150ml (5½fl oz/⅔ cup) coconut oil, melted

Equipment

High-powered blender

Clean muslin (cheesecloth)

Rubber band or string

20cm (8in) round or square baking tin

FERMENTED CASHEW BASE Blend the soaked and rinsed
cashews with the water in a high-powered blender until silky
smooth, scraping down the blender jug a few times with a
spatula and blending until you have a smooth mix (see page 16
for blender etiquette). Transfer to a sterilized large glass jar or
bowl and make sure it is room temperature before stirring in
the ginger bug or kombucha. Cover the jar or bowl with a loose
lid or clean cloth, secure with string or a rubber band and leave
somewhere ambient in your kitchen to ferment overnight (do
not put the mixture in the fridge). The next day the mixture
should be lightly aerated and ready for the next step.

CHESTNUT BISCUIT BASE Put the flours in a large mixing bowl
with the salt, sugar and cubed butter or oil. Lightly rub the
mixture between your fingertips until the mixture resembles
breadcrumbs, lightly shaking the bowl from side to side to bring
any lumps to the surface and continuing to rub until there
are none left. Add the coconut yoghurt and bring the mixture
together using a spoon, then start lightly kneading with your
hands. It should form a smooth dough.

Preheat the oven to 180°C fan/200°C/400°F/gas 6 and line
the base and sides of a round or square baking tin with some
baking parchment.

Dust a clean surface with flour and roll out the dough to a
thickness of 5mm (¼ inch), or just press the dough into the base
of the tin and use the back of the spoon to make it smooth. Prick
the pastry with a fork and bake for 15–20 minutes until golden.
Remove from the oven and let it cool in the tin.

GINGER CREAM Blend the fermented cashew base with the
almond milk, lemon juice, sweetener and fresh ginger until
silky smooth. Add the rest of the spices, the salt and lemon
zest and blend again. Finally, stream in the melted cacao butter
and coconut oil while the motor's running and blend until well
combined. Pour the ginger cream onto the baked and cooled
chestnut pastry and set in the fridge for at least 4 hours.

Once firm to touch, cut the cake into roughly 12 pieces
and enjoy.

NUT BUTTER BARS

These pecan butter bars are your official lesson in caramel. This recipe can be adapted with any of the raw or cooked set caramels on page 159 for different but still delicious results. These bars were an all-time favourite with my recipe testers who tried them with different types of nut and seed butters. Explore for yourself and see how straightforward it can be to make a caramel bar with only natural and whole ingredients.

Makes: 5 bars

Time taken: 45 minutes, plus 1 hour and 30 minutes to set

For the caramel

1 batch of Date Caramel or Set Caramel* (page 159)

For the toasted coconut base

200g (7oz) coconut flakes (not desiccated, as it's much drier)

½ tsp sea salt

50g (1¾oz) cacao nibs (optional)

For the enrobing chocolate

2 tbsp Nut or Seed Butter (page 41) of your choice

300g (10½oz) vegan dark chocolate (75-80% cocoa), melted

Equipment

High-powered blender

*With both caramels you have the choice of nut or seed butter. Opt for pecan butter as the ultimate indulgence, almond for a crowd-pleaser, sunflower for a surprise or peanut for a classic flavour combination.

Make your chosen caramel, see page 159.

TOASTED COCONUT BASE Lightly toast the coconut flakes in a large frying pan over a medium heat until beautiful golden, moving them constantly so they do not burn. Let them cool slightly off the heat and then, while they are still warm, put them in a high-powered blender and blend to a butter. Once smooth, add the salt and blend once more. If you are using cacao nibs, lightly toast them in the frying pan after the coconut, leave to cool slightly and pulse through the coconut butter at the end of blending.

Line the base and sides of a small, deep tray or airtight plastic container with baking paper and pour the coconut butter into the lined tray, spreading it out evenly to cover the base of the tray – ideally it should be 1cm (½ inch) thick. Set in the fridge for 20 minutes and then top with the caramel and transfer to the freezer for at least 1 hour, until firm to touch.

ENROBING CHOCOLATE Fold the nut or seed butter through the melted chocolate and keep warm in a small bowl (the smaller the bowl the better, so it is easier to dip the bars). Cut the bar mix into five 1.5cm (½ inch)-wide bars, trimming off the ends to make them neat (and enjoying the offcuts as a chef snack!). Line a baking tray with baking paper and, using a fork, carefully lower the bars one by one, submerging them in the chocolate, then tapping off any excess chocolate on the side of the bowl and placing them on the lined tray. Set in the fridge for 10 more minutes, then enjoy!

These will keep in the fridge for up to 1 week or the freezer for 1 month.

PLATING 101

Plating is the final step of putting together any dish, and is sometimes overlooked and often overthought. Some have the visual idea of a dish before they finalize the flavours, others can only visualize it when the flavours of a dish are complete. But when something is nicely put together it will always make for a more enjoyable eating experience. You don't need to follow all these guidelines, but just putting more attention into how you plate your food will make a difference.

Plating is subjective, and while styles come and go, the classics last; the organic, free-flowing and simple creations that showcase ingredients as they are meant to be. With natural plant-based food our plates tell that story, without being overly complicated, fiddled with or fussy. My plating mentor said that 'the ingredients should look like they have gracefully fallen onto the plate' and I always say in my classes that when plating you must commit to where you have put things, and, like Coco Chanel once said, 'always take off the last thing you put on'.

Throughout this book you will see my personal plating style. It's just one of many ways to do things, none of which are right or wrong, but all of them exist to inspire you and share different creative expressions. My (Plant Academy) way tends to be more organic in appearance (no lines or dots) with elements grouped together: fresh elements (herbs, leaves and plants) and worked into elements (sauces and oils), and gently using off-white ceramic and round(ish) plates.

Following these guidelines will help any plate look appealing. They are a great place to start, but it is important to master your own style.

ELEMENTS OF PLATING

THE PLATE ITSELF

The plate is your canvas and it's a good idea to match the feeling of the dish with the style of the plate. For example, an organic and colourful plant-based dish may work well on a handmade natural ceramic plate, a rich and dark dish maybe in a deeper-coloured bowl, a classic flavour combination may work best on a plain and classic plate. Consider colours, textures and feelings.

COLOUR

Is your dish one colour and therefore needs some contrast? Maybe the ingredients are very colourful and need a plain canvas? Think about the colour of your elements and the plate that will enable them to shine.

ODD NUMBERS

Using odd numbers of each element guides the eye naturally around a plate. For example, if you put two tomatoes on a plate your eye bounces just from one to another, whereas if there are three you have a more flowing feel. This idea applies too when you are plating something such as the cannelloni on page 176, or there may be three areas of icing on a cake or three tomatoes on some savoury pancakes.

NEGATIVE SPACE

Leave empty space around the ingredients so you can see what you're about to eat, rather than adding swirls of sauces or sprinkles of seeds over everything. Place ingredients in groups, with ingredients such as seeds or dressing in set places next to what you intend for them to be eaten with.

HEIGHT

Plates of food will always look more attractive if they have some height, rather than being totally flat against the surface. Think about using dried elements, leaves and herbs to add life to a dish.

OFF CENTRE

This rule doesn't apply to everything – something like a tart may look just right in the centre of the plate, or equally a tasty salad gathered in the centre – but the off-centre invitation is here to invite you to allow things to look more natural and to play around with making playful plates.

TOPPING A CAKE OR TART

When it comes to cakes or tarts, it is important for the topping to balance out the flavours at the bottom. For example, if you have a cake or tart with a textured, biscuity, crunchy pastry and a smooth and creamy filling – which most likely holds the main flavour of the dish – any toppings are there to add a pop of flavour or texture to the other layers. In this instance, you might use one area of toppings or maybe three, following a pattern and explaining to the eater what you want them to eat with what. So, perhaps you have one dot of icing with one cluster of candied seeds and one *relevant* flower petal, repeating this in three mini areas.

RADISHES & SEED BUTTER

Fresh, Pickled & Baked Radish With
Whipped Seed Butter

This is such a fun dish to make. It's simple and colourful, and
an ideal example of how to present something in an interesting
way. With layers of fresh, fermented, salty, acidic and creamy
elements, this dish naturally leads the eater around the plate,
guiding them on what to eat together.

Serves: 4 as a small plate

Time taken: 30 minutes, plus 2 days pickling

For the pickled radish

4 medium radishes, washed and dried

75ml (2½fl oz/5 tbsp) apple cider or vegan
white wine vinegar

1 tsp sea salt

1 tbsp honey or agave syrup

75ml (2½fl oz/5 tbsp) filtered water

1 star anise

5 pink peppercorns (or black if pink aren't
available)

For the whipped butter

40g (1½oz) sunflower Seed Butter (page 41, or
tahini or cashew butter)

40g (1½oz) fermented cashews (page 113) or
cashew cream (page 158)

2½ tbsp almond or sunflower milk

20g (¾oz) coconut oil (deodorized*) or cacao
butter, melted

1 tsp lemon juice

1 tsp nutritional yeast

½ tsp sea salt

For the baked radish

4 medium radishes, washed and dried

2 tbsp olive oil

½ tsp sea salt

To serve

1 raw radish (perhaps in a different colour),
washed and thinly sliced

Micro herbs, such as dill or nasturtiums

Sea salt or charcoal salt (for a wonderful
appearance and taste)

Equipment

500ml (17fl oz) sterilized glass jar

Hand-held electric whisk (optional)

*This is a coconut oil without the flavour, useful
for recipes where the coconut flavour is not
required but you still need a setting agent.

PICKLED RADISH Cut away the root and top/leaves of the radishes, keeping them whole. Place a small saucepan over a medium heat and add the vinegar, salt, honey or agave, water and spices. Simmer until the salt and sweetener are dissolved, then turn off the heat. Put the radishes in the jar, pour over the hot pickling liquid and leave to cool, then seal with the lid and leave to pickle at room temperature for 12 hours, then in the fridge for 1–2 days.

WHIPPED BUTTER Put the seed butter, fermented cashews and plant milk in a medium bowl and whisk together with a hand-held electric whisk or a standard whisk. Once the mixture is combined, add the melted oil or cacao butter, lemon juice, nutritional yeast and salt and whisk again to make a smooth fluffy butter. Refrigerate until ready to serve.

BAKED RADISH Once the radish pickles are ready, preheat the oven to 180°C fan/200°C/400°F/gas 6 and line a baking tray with baking paper. Cut away the root and leaves of the radishes (if the leaves are small and tender, keep them for garnishing), then halve them from top to bottom. Toss them in the oil and salt then place on the lined baking tray cut side facing down. Bake in the oven for 10 minutes, then turn each radish and bake for another 5–10 minutes until they are wonderfully golden.

To make one plate: remove one pickled radish from the brine and thinly slice it.

Place a spoonful of the butter on the plate then layer the raw, baked and pickled radish around the butter, garnish with micro herbs (and radish tops, if using) and sprinkle with salt (charcoal for the optimum effect).

COURGETTE CANNELLONI

With Lemon Ricotta, Harissa & Parsley Oil

This recipe has just a few simple elements yet comes together in a creative way. This plating style is more artsy than most dishes in this book but it's a great example of using the plating guidelines. Height, colour, negative space and odd numbers all come into play, and visually explain how the dish is intended to be eaten. This is a good dish for exploring plating styles, as the elements hold well and can come together in lots of different ways.

Serves: 2–4

Time taken: 15 minutes, plus 4 hours soaking time

For the lemon ricotta

200g (7oz) cashews, soaked for 4 hours in filtered water then drained and rinsed

100ml (3½fl oz/scant ½ cup) filtered water

50ml (1½fl oz/3½ tbsp) olive oil

2 tbsp finely chopped and deseeded preserved lemon (fine brunoise)

¼–½ tsp sea salt (depending on how salty the lemons are, or use 1–2 tsp of preserved lemon brine)

To serve

1 large courgette (zucchini)

1 batch Romesco Sauce (page 35)

10 fresh multi-coloured cherry tomatoes, halved and quartered

30g (1oz) fresh herbs such as dill or red sorrel

Tomato Skin Crisps (page 129) (optional)

2–4 tbsp Savoury Granola (page 70) (optional)

60–90ml (2–3fl oz/4–6 tbsp) Parsley Oil (page 30)

Equipment

High-powered blender

LEMON RICOTTA Put the soaked and rinsed cashews in a high-powered blender with the water and blend until smooth (do not put in all of the water straight away, persevere without adding too much water as this is the filling of the cannelloni and you don't want it to be too loose). Add the oil and blend once more until smooth. Fold in the preserved lemon and salt and store in the fridge for up to 4 days until ready to serve.

CANNELLONI Prepare the courgette by cutting away the top and end, then, using either a vegetable peeler or mandoline, cut it into long thin strips about 2mm (⅛ inch) thick – this will be the 'cannelloni'. Lay the strips on a chopping board, then place 1 tablespoon of the lemon ricotta mixture at one end of each strip and roll the courgette strips around the filling.

Plate, with the Romesco around the edge or in a circle at the centre of the plate, and 3–5 'cannellonis', filled with fresh tomatoes next to each cannelloni. Add fresh herbs, following the lines of the cannelloni, add tomato crisps and/or savoury granola in three places in between the other elements but not covering them and a few spoons of parsley oil just in between the cannelloni so it beautifully spills out onto the plate.

TIP – Serve on crackers as a canapé, as part of a salad spread, or alongside cooked elements such as quinoa if you want a more substantial plate.

NUT & SEED SOAKING TIMES

The following are general guidelines for soaking and sprouting.

NUTS

NUT	FLAVOUR	SOAKING TIME	UPP (UNIQUE PLANT POWER)	TOP NUTRITIONAL BENEFITS
Almonds	Sweet, earthy	8–12 hours	The most popular plant milk in the world. Almonds are extremely versatile	Raw almonds are a rich source of vitamin E as well as calcium, iron and magnesium
Brazil nuts	Woody, bitter-sweet	8 hours	A brazil nut milk makes a fantastic hot chocolate, and brazil nut butter is even more interesting in savoury dishes	Brazil nuts are especially rich in monounsaturated fatty acids and a good source of selenium
Cashew nuts	Sweet, creamy	4–6 hours	Extra creamy and exceptionally good for cheeses, yoghurts, sweet and savoury creams	Cashews have a high content of monounsaturated fats with minerals including copper, magnesium, thiamine, calcium and niacin
Hazelnuts	Distinct nuttiness, earthly	8 hours	The perfect pairing to anything made with cacao	Rich in protein and unsaturated fat with amounts of thiamine and B vitamins; it can be ground into flour
Macadamia nuts	Sweet, mellow and creamy	7–12 hours	Second in the running after cashew for making the best cheeses, versatile milks and creams	Rich in monounsaturated fat and a good source of dietary fibre

Pecans	Caramel sweetness	4–6 hours	One of the sweetest nuts, pecans make the most incredible roasted nut butters and candies. Yet when you turn them into milk they become more savoury	Pecans contain oleic acid, vitamins, minerals and dietary fibre. Pecans, recognized for neurological protection, are ranked the highest of all nuts in antioxidants
Pine nuts	Savoury, buttery	2 hours	Traditionally known for their key part in a classic pesto, have you ever thought of making a pine nut cream? Pine nuts work really well in sweet dishes and make a smooth chantilly and delicious milk base for drinks	Pine nuts are high in protein and fat with amino acids. The American 'pinion' variety is a high source of vitamin B1 and European pignoli are a great source of iron
Pistachio nuts	Distinct nuttiness, grass, earth	6 hours	Work well as a base for savoury dressings but can also be used in ice creams, desserts or candied as a great addition to a sweet or savoury dish	Pistachios contain two unique antioxidants not often found in other nuts: lutein, and zeaxanthin. These have been associated with eye health and risk reduction for developing age-related macular degeneration
Walnuts	Buttery, earthly, bitter	8 hours	The nut that looks like a brain and is good for your brain. Walnuts are incredibly rich and become like liquid gold when turned into butter	Considered a 'brain food' with their high concentration of omega-3 fats, variety of vitamins and minerals, walnuts are recognized for cardiovascular protection and improved mental function
Peanuts	Woody, earthy, sweet, smoky	4 hours	From a culinary perspective they have a great taste but in the Plant Academy pantry we use them sparingly, just for big pops of flavour and nostalgic desserts	Technically a legume, peanuts are known prolifically for peanut butter, but if you do a little digging they aren't the healthiest of breakfast companions as they tend to be high in mould and can cause inflammation in the body

SEEDS

SEED	FLAVOUR	SOAKING TIME	UPP (UNIQUE PLANT POWER)	TOP NUTRITIONAL BENEFITS
Hemp seeds	Grassy, creamy	No soaking needed!	Hulled hemp seeds make instant milk, just blend and go, no soaking or straining required!	Hemp seeds also are the best seed for your brain health, boasting high omega content. Plus they are grown in Europe easily and efficiently
Pumpkin seeds	Deep, grassy	1–2 hours	Pumpkin seeds are an incredibly nutrient dense, flavour rich seed. With their dark green colour they make a unique milk and butter	Pumpkin seeds are a natural source of tryptophan, an amino acid that promotes sleep
Sunflower seeds	Earthly, soft	1–2 hours	They are the seed equivalent to a cashew in terms of versatility	They can be sprouted from dry (see page 54), grow into extremely nutritious sprouts and they can also be a great addition to a nut butter, wonderful candy or a stable cream

Sesame seeds	Earthy, sweet and bitter all at once	1 hour	Maybe the most famous seed, used in spice blends, as tahini and in many cultural dishes especially in the Middle East	A great source of calcium in plant-based diets
Chia seeds	Neutral	30 minutes (to gel), do not rinse	Chia seeds are in the family of more gelatinous ingredients that can help things to bind together	As well as being a hero ingredient in seed-based breads, breakfasts and desserts, chia seeds are very fun to sprout and so easy to bring to life! (see sprouting, chapter 3)
Flax seeds	Nutty, mellow	15 minutes (to gel), do not rinse	In plant-based food we use them to bind things together and to make what is called a 'flax egg', find out more on page 149	Known to support gut health when made into a gelatinous tea. Also known for their high protein and omega content, often found in protein powders

ABOUT THE AUTHOR & CONTRIBUTORS

LAUREN LOVATT is a plant-based chef, culinary educator and entrepreneur who founded Plant Academy cookery school in 2019, a school created to inspire passion through plants through inviting the leading minds in the industry to teach their signature Plant 123 chef training program. As well as a passion for plants, Lauren's main focus is bringing the conversation of mental health to the table through her revolutionary book *Mind Food*, released in 2022, after many years of curating supper clubs, hosting events at festivals, such as Wilderness and Shambla, and leading retreats on this important topic. Lauren trained in LA and NYC, led the PlantLab Barcelona School, ran Asparagasm in the Cotswolds and now teaches with Alchemy Academy in Bali. She has traveled and taught Plant Academy courses and retreats around the world including in Bali, Norway, Spain and in the US, and curated the food concept for Paris' first plant-based hotel, HOY, and their restaurant Mesa. Lauren is forever evolving her own food art and conscious impact on the food world. She can be found on Instagram @plantacademylondon / @lauren_lovatt.

SARA KIYO POPOWA is a photographer, recipe developer and influencer as @shisodelicious. She is the popular author of *Bento Power* and *The Opinionated Guide to Vegan London*. Sara has been an integral part of Plant Academy since the beginning, first coming on board to teach masterclasses about her book *Bento Power* and photography and going on to open a joint venture with Lauren Lovatt 'The Food Studio' where they created the Plant Academy online courses and so much more. Sara's passion for plants and incredible photography skills brought Plant Academy to life in a brand new way and all of the photos and animations for the courses, online and for this Plant Academy book, have been created by her over the last four years. She shares with Lovatt a devotion to the power of the visual and for communicating plant-based food in a mesmerizingly bold and aesthetic way. This book and all of Plant Academy would not be the same without her.

SOPHIE DUNSTER is an illustrator and founder of sustainable lifestyle brand Gung Ho London. She specializes in storytelling through design and communication. At the core of all her work, Sophie jam-packs artwork and design with meaningful messaging to inspire change and get people talking about current issues. In 2019, she launched her 'Food for Thought' collection, exploring our food system and how the things we eat impact the planet. This connected Sophie with Lauren through a shared passion for making a positive impact on the food world. Together they have run many food, art and fashion events and Sophie's mission to inspire through design continues with Gung Ho London, as well as also helping other brands and businesses communicate what they do in creative ways. From interiors to uniforms and bespoke artwork, check out Sophie's work at sophiedunster.co.uk and gungholondon.com.

RICHARD BUCKLEY was raised a vegetarian and, after graduating with a degree in English Literature, he set about studying vegetable cookery whilst working in a series of top vegetarian restaurants. This culminated in his five-year role as head chef for Demuth's Restaurant where he developed and refined his plant-centric cooking style. He has a passion for sharing the knowledge and techniques that he has learnt and developed in order to increase the general standard of vegan cookery across the country. His restaurants, including Michelin-starred OAK Restaurant in Bath, have been featured in multiple national publications including *The Independent*, *The Telegraph*, *The Times*, *olive magazine*, *Vegetarian Living*, *Stylist* and *Vogue*. He gets a steady stream of famous customers through its doors including Rufus Wainwright, Thom Yorke, Jeanette Winterson, Nick Knowles, Mel Giedroyc and Kevin McCloud. He is the author of the cookbook *Plants Taste Better*. Richard was the first guest to be a part of Plant Academy London and has since taught on Plant 123, bringing his creative visual and culinary techniques to our classrooms. We are forever grateful for Richard's support and collaboration.

CAROLINA CHINEA is a dedicated advocate for plant-based living from the picturesque Canary Islands. Since 2007, she has travelled the world as a plant-based business trainer, designing innovative projects and educational experiences. She is passionate about cultivating creativity in plant-based living, nourishing minds and empowering businesses. With a background in art history, Carolina has curated over 100 workshops, co-created the Plant Academy Plant 123 program alongside Lauren and collaborated with schools like Matthew Kenney, Plant Academy, Aurea and Alchemy. Carolina has brought concepts to life from Evergreen Organics in Qatar to Vibe in Cambodia, and her expertise in plant-based cuisine includes product development and chef training. Her qualifications from Matthew Kenney Culinary and Hofmann Culinary School underpin

her work in creating unique food experiences. She empowers individuals to express themselves through the universal language of food using methodologies such as Design Thinking.

RACHEL DE THAMPLE is an award-winning author who has worked in food, health and sustainability for more than 20 years. She teaches fermentation and seasonal nutrition courses at River Cottage in the United Kingdom as well as many masterclasses with Plant Academy. She served as Course Director of the College of Naturopathic Medicine's Natural Chef diploma course, was the Head of Food for the British organic retailer Abel & Cole and Commissioning Editor of Waitrose Food Illustrated. She's written seven books including *Tonics & Teas* and *Fermentation: River Cottage Handbook*, which won a Guild of Food Writer's Award. Her latest book is *Winter Wellness*, hailed as 'a remarkable addition to the world of cookbooks' by René Redzepi, chef and co-owner of noma. She's also studied sustainable food systems at University College London and was instrumental in setting up an award-winning food market in London.

ARTHUR POTTS DAWSON has been cooking for 37 years, and is Head of Strategic Partnerships

and Sustainability at Feed Me Seymour, Executive Chef at Omved Gardens in London and a UN World Food Program Advocacy Chef. Arthur has taught on Plant Academy courses with his 'Missing Ingredient' class which inspired the chapter in this book. A Sustainable Food Innovator who demands change and reimagines the connections that food has with the world, Arthur makes old food styles new again with an approach that revisits a gentler, less aggressive way to produce, serve and eat food. With strategic policy creation and thought leadership in sustainable food, Arthur looks at the importance of ethical and human food connections. Arthur is a chef, a foodie, a teacher, a mentor, a social entrepreneur, a business founder and, as an environmentalist, loves being disruptively creative within the food industry. Much of his thinking is how we can minimize the impact that food businesses have on the planet, what the future of food is and where restaurants need to improve to lower their customers' negative consumption habits on the planet.

INDEX

ACKNOWLEDGEMENTS

Plant Academy has always been a team effort and came to be thanks to so many people along the way.

To David Bez, for the initial collaboration idea, contribution to the original space and for his ongoing passion for plants.

To everyone who supported our Kickstarter in 2018, these pledges got us off the ground and made Plant Academy a reality.

To Carolina Chinea, for truly understanding the vision for Plant Academy and being able to bring it to life and to the next level with her creativity and skills. Truly the greatest collaboration we could have ever wished for.

To all of our teachers onsite and online, these collaborations have made Plant Academy what it is.

By sharing ideas, recipes and audiences, we are stronger because of all of you (see page 191).

Especially to Richard Buckley, who truly understood the Plant Academy concept from the start and whose confidence in us motivated me even more to do everything we have done.

To Sara Kiyo Popowa, our partner in food. Sara's attention to detail and incredible skills in photography and food styling, as well as her deep awareness and understanding of plants and impactful communication, have made Plant Academy and this book understood visually in a way we could never have dreamed of.

To Sophie Dunster, our illustrator within these pages. Sophie's 'Gung Ho' attitude is always a treat to be around. Her playful illustrations have given a new layer to *Plant Academy: The Cookbook* like no other person could have.

To everyone who has been a part of my Plant Academy team over the years, especially Jasmin Howarth, who has been an integral part of the most recent part of Plant Academy with her amazing organizational skills, and also for testing many of these recipes.

Of course to my parents who always believe in my wild ideas, have attended courses and events and are always cheering me on from the sidelines, thank you.

RECOMMENDED READING

David Bez, *Salad Love*
David Bez, *Vegan Love*
Richard Buckley, *Plants Taste Better*
Natasha Corrett and Vicki Edgson, *Honestly Healthy*
Rachel de Thample, *Fermentation: River Cottage Handbook No.18*
Rachel de Thample, *Tonics & Teas*

Rachel de Thample, *Winter Wellness*
Naomi Devlin, *Food for a Happy Gut*
Doug Evans, *The Sprout Book*
Tom Hunt, *The Natural Cook: Eating the Seasons from Root to Fruit*
Alicia Kennedy, *No Meat Required*
Sara Kiyo Popowa, *Bento Power*

Zoë Lind van't Hof and Tom Smale (Wunder Workshop), *Super Root Spices*
Lauren Lovatt, *Mind Food*
Douglas McMaster, *Silo: The Zero Waste Blueprint*
Julie Piatt, *This Cheese is Nuts!*
Chad Sarno, Derek Sarno and David Joachim, *Wicked Healthy*

PLANT ACADEMY PEOPLE

True pioneers of plant-forward cooking who have been an integral part of Plant Academy must be credited here and researched if you're interested:

CAROLINA CHINEA, plant-based business coach, chef and co-creator of Plant Academy

RICHARD BUCKLEY, author of *Plants Taste Better* and founder of Acorn and OAK restaurants in Bath

ARTHUR POTTS DAWSON, the original green chef, World Food Program Advocacy Chef for the UN and co-author of the Chefs' Manifesto.

SARA KIYO POPOWA, author of *Bento Power*, creator of @shisodelicious and our Plant Academy photographer (and photographer of this book!)

RACHEL DE THAMPLE, author, teacher and fermenter

KIRK HAWORTH, chef and creator of the concept Plates

DOUGLAS MCMASTER, founder of Silo London and author of *Silo: The Zero Waste Blueprint*

JOHNNY DRAIN, fermentation mastermind and scientist; a pioneer in the fermentation field

TOM HUNT, food activist, author and founder of Poco; Tom champions root-to-fruit eating and a sustainable plate

KATE MAGIC, raw food legend, founder of Raw Living and author of many books

AMY LEVIN, raw chocolate master and dessert artist, known around the world for her food artistry and high-level techniques

NAOMI DEVLIN, gluten-free baker known for her next level gluten-free teaching

JASON WOOD, chef, food consultant and co-creator of @stellar__plants

AYELEN MARTINEZ, our resident shroom and founder of Oh My Shrooms

WUNDER WORKSHOP, founders Zoe and Tom have created magical products shining a light on the power of adaptogens and potent plants

BRISTOL FUNGARIUM, pioneers in the UK for homegrown medicinal mushrooms

THE CHEFS' MANIFESTO, an incredible chef-led project that brings together more than 1500 chefs from around the world to explore how they can help deliver a sustainable food system

DEDICATION

To Plant Academy students past, present and future, thank you. I couldn't have made this book possible without your ongoing support.

Quarto

First published in 2025 by Leaping Hare Press,
an imprint of The Quarto Group.
One Triptych Place
London, SE1 9SH,
United Kingdom
T (0)20 7700 6700 / www.Quarto.com

A catalogue record for this book is available from the British
Library.

ISBN 978-0-7112-9048-8
Ebook ISBN 978-0-7112-9049-5

10 9 8 7 6 5 4 3 2 1

Design by Georgie Hewitt
Photography by Sara Kiyo Popowa
Illustrations by Sophie Dunster
Commissioned by Monica Perdoni
Edited by Katerina Menhennet
Senior Designer Renata Latipova
Production Controller Rohana Yusof

Printed in Bosnia and Herzegovina

The information in this book is based on the author's personal experience and opinions. It is not intended to diagnose or prevent any illness or condition and is not a substitute for advice from a counsellor, physician, or other health care professional. Knowledge of nutrition and mental health is constantly evolving and you are encouraged to consult other sources and make independent judgments about the issues discussed. There is the possibility of allergic or other adverse reactions from the use of certain ingredients. You should seek the advice of your doctor or other qualified health provider with any questions you may have. You should not delay seeking counselling, medical or other professional help or advice because of something you have read in this book or use the information in this book as a substitute for medication or other treatment prescribed by your doctor.

The author and publisher make no representations or warranties with respect to the accuracy, completeness or fitness for a particular purpose of the contents of this book and exclude all liability to the extent permitted by law for any errors or omissions and for any loss, damage or expense (whether direct or indirect) suffered by anyone relying on any information contained in this book.